Biblical St
Performances

Stories, Plays, Songs, Musicals

Compiled by Rebecca Daniel

illustrated by
Corbin Hillam

Cover by Janet Skiles

A Division of Good Apple, Inc.
ISBN No. 0-86653-492-X
Standardized Subject Code TA ac
Printing No. 987654321

Shining Star Publications
A Division of Good Apple, Inc.
Box 299
Carthage, IL 62321-0299

Unless otherwise indicated, the King James Version of the Bible was used in preparing the activities in this book.

TO THE TEACHER/PARENT

Have you ever wished you could make Bible stories come alive for your children? If you have, *Biblical Story Performances* is perfect for you. When children perform the stories and memorize the lines, the Christian lessons become part of their being. The values are suddenly relevant and biblical history is transformed into a meaningful learning experience for all. This book contains stories, plays, and songs to make dozens of Bible stories much more than history. From Adam and Eve to the Resurrection of Jesus, characters including Daniel, David, Elijah, Noah, Moses and Queen Esther, plus twenty-two others, are explored in these original stories, songs, and plays.

Presentations become easy with the step-by-step directions, reproducible scripts and music, tips for turning stories into performances, creative costume directions and reproducible graphics for scenery and backdrops found in *Biblical Story Performances.* So whether you are planning an informal Bible story lesson for a small group of students or a musical extravaganza to be delivered to a whole congregation or school, on a stage with costumes and scenery, your performance is guaranteed to dazzle everyone and have them standing in ovation with the original stories, plays and songs found herein.

TABLE OF CONTENTS

SS1870

BIBLE STORIES

PERFORMING A STORY

HOW TO TURN A STORY INTO A PERFORMANCE

by Helen Kitchell Evans

Reading stories to children presents a fine language experience. They never tire hearing the story repeated several times. As you re-read, let the children begin to tell the story with you. In a short time, they will be able to do it on their own.

Give each child a copy of the story. After it becomes a part of their thinking, start new activities. Begin by asking who the characters were in the story and what part they played in its development. Discuss the number of characters. Write their names on the blackboard as the discussion continues.

Introduce the idea of writing a play based on the story. Let the children decide who in the class might be able to take the parts of these characters.

Tell the children to write their own plays. At the end of the assigned time for writing, have the children read their plays to the class. Perhaps some may wish to assign parts and dramatize their little plays. Then select the best from all plays and write a play as a class project. Give the children a copy of this final play.

OTHER FOLLOW-UP ACTIVITIES:

PANTOMIME

A reader sets the scenes for the story. As he/she continues, the classmates act out the story.

SHADOW PICTURES

Place a light behind a large white sheet stretched open. Darken the room as much as possible. The actors move back and forth between the sheet and the light. Between scenes the light is put out or covered while the reader announces the next scene.

READER'S THEATER

This is presented as a play but all parts are read. This is a good way to introduce the use of a microphone (radio drama).

CHORAL READING

Have the children write sentences about the story. Arrange in sequence. Assign parts to various children. Suggested ways to present choral readings:

1. Line-a-child; 2. With solo parts; 3. Divide into two groups, I and II, assigning lines to each group; 4. Add a line for the entire group to speak. This is called the chorus. Example: If the story was about Moses, the choral response could be: Moses lead his people! (This would be spoken after Group I and again after Group II.)

PUZZLES

Based on the story, work out different kinds of puzzles. Good project for older students.

FINGER PLAYS

Younger children love finger plays. Let older children help them work out a simple finger play based on the story.

ACTION RHYMES

Write a class rhyme with a beat that could be used for jumping rope. Example: Moses lead the people away. They followed Moses every day.

BULLETIN BOARD

Draw pictures and slogans to advertise the play if you wish to plan a special presentation for others. Make invitations and design tickets.

VIDEO TAPE THE PLAYS

File these video tapes to be used in future classwork.

TABLEAU (living pictures)

Group various characters in a picturesque scene. The group stands costumed and posed while a narrator comments on the scene. Curtain may be opened and closed; or a large frame can be made that group stands within.

BOOK REPORTS

Think of the story as a small book. Give a book report to the class.

OPERETTA

Use the play interspersed with the songs in this book to form an operetta. This could be a real special celebration for parents and all students in the school.

DRAWINGS

Draw pictures, then use an overhead projector to enlarge the drawings upon large sheets of paper. Color, paste on cardboard, cut out and make stage background for real or puppet shows. Make a mural for the classroom. Use the projector or large freehand drawings.

QUESTIONS

Ask questions about the story and have children either write in their own words or find the line in the text of the story that gives the answer. Good constructive seatwork.

REVERSE STORIES

Often children are shown pictures in a book and told to write the story they see as they read the pictures. Reverse this idea. Hear the story and draw the pictures.

CRAFTS

If the story presents an idea that could be used for crafts, let the children think what could be made and what materials would be needed. Examples: Baskets to go with a story about the five loaves and fishes. A mobile of fish, etc. Large milk cartons make good baskets.

LETTER WRITING

Write a letter to the pastor or Sunday school teacher telling about the stories they are working on in class.

SHOW AND TELL

Make something at home that is suggested by the story. Bring items to school for a surprise afternoon party.

POEMS

Try writing poems about the story. Even the youngest can rhyme two lines and it is a wonderful way to train little minds for the enjoyment of poetry as they progress in school.

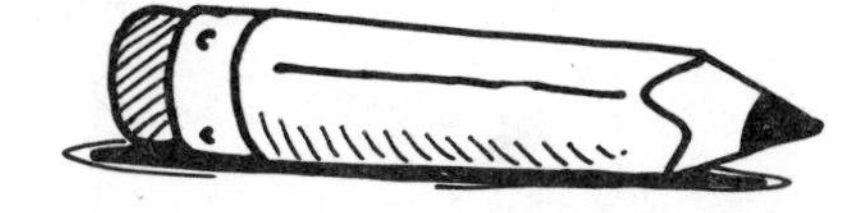

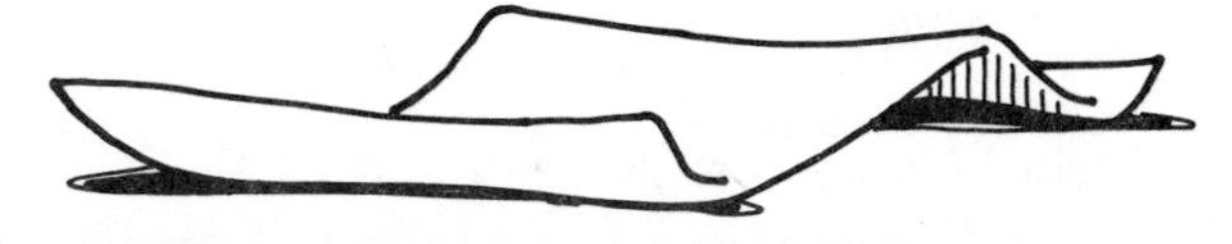

A GIFT FOR JASON

by Rosemary Baker

"Where are all those people going?" Jason asked himself as he looked down towards the bottom of the grassy hillside upon which he was seated. "I think that I'll follow and see."

Picking up his wooden crutch and leather knapsack, Jason put the crutch under his right arm and slung the knapsack over his left shoulder. He hobbled slowly down the hill, dragging his right food behind him, and headed toward the large crowd of men, women and children walking on the sandy beach of the Jordan River.

After a while, the crowd stopped and began to sit down in a grassy area near a low mountain, upon which there were several standing figures of men.

As Jason neared, he could see the men upon the mountain clearly, and he counted thirteen men. Twelve of the men were circled around a man dressed in white. He seemed to be their leader.

Ten-year-old Jason quickly found a spot of grass to sit down upon. He put his crutch and knapsack beside him and waited to see what was to happen.

The people grew quiet and the man in white started to speak. He talked about the love of God and His kingdom.

As Jason listened, he whispered to a young man seated by him, "Who is this man?"

"His name is Jesus and He has healed many people who were ill. These people are here today hoping to be healed; or have brought their relatives or friends to be healed," the young man whispered back.

When Jason heard this, he looked down toward his twisted right food and thought, If only He would heal my crippled foot so I could walk without a crutch! I wonder if His heavenly Father would let Him if he knew about me? But who am I to be asking for healing when I'm only a lowly shepherd boy not worthy to be healed!

As the hours went by, the people and Jason listened to the words of Jesus.

At different times, many people who were blind, deaf or crippled were healed instantly! They would stand up as they were healed and made well. They would wave their arms toward heaven and give thanks to God. How Jason longed to be one of them!

Finally twilight time was nearing, and as the sun went down toward the top of the near-by purple hills, a murmur went through the crowd. Jason heard a whisper saying, "It's time for our evening meal, and there's no food to eat. What shall we do?"

Jason thought about the problem, and then he decided, Perhaps I can help a little. He picked up his crutch and knapsack and hobbled slowly toward a large man standing near Jesus. He tugged gently on the sleeve of the man's robe.

"Yes?" asked the man as he turned toward Jason.

"Please, sir," said Jason as he offered his knapsack to the man, "I have a little food in here that you may have to help feed these people, if you wish. It isn't much, only five barley loaves of bread and two small fish. My mother gave them to me to take to my two brothers who are herding sheep in the mountains, but you are welcome to use them!"

As Jason spoke, Jesus walked over to him and stood before him. Jason looked up into His beautiful face, let his crutch fall to the ground, and fell down upon his knees before Him. Bowing his head, Jason asked, "Oh, Jesus, will you heal me, please? I have been crippled all of my life, and I would so like to be able to walk and run as others do! Will Your heavenly Father possibly help me too?"

Jesus put his right hand softly upon Jason's head and prayed.

Instantly a feeling of warmth went through Jason's right foot. As he opened his eyes and watched, his crippled foot straightened and became as perfect as his left foot. He was healed! A miracle had happened!

"I have two good feet!" Jason shouted. "Look at me! I don't need my crutch anymore!" He stood up quickly and walked around to show everyone that he could walk. He wasn't a cripple anymore!

Then Jason lifted his arms toward heaven and gave God and Jesus thanks for his wonderful gift of love!

Filled with happiness, Jason turned and ran for the first time in his life toward his home in Bethsaida to tell his family and friends all about Jesus, and the gift that had been given to him.

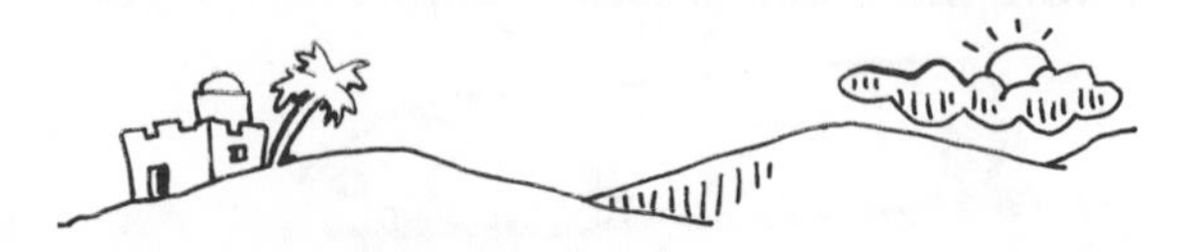

THE MYSTERIOUS BOY

by Virginia L. Kroll

Hannah and her sister Marah were awake early this morning. They loved laundry day at the lake. Many of the villagers congregated there. The atmosphere was a welcome change from the hot, dusty township.

"Take Caleb with you," Mama suggested. "The air will do him good."

Hannah and Marah exchanged glances. They didn't think anything would help Caleb, but they certainly would not argue with Mama.

Hannah loaded the donkey with the laundry baskets on either side and then saddled him for Caleb. With Mama's help, she strapped him securely into the saddle. Marah packed the lunches, and the three set out for the lake.

Caleb hadn't been born right. His head rolled from side to side with a will of its own. His arms and legs jerked, and he drooled while making sounds that no one but Mama ever understood.

The girls led the donkey to their favorite lakeside spot. The breeze rippled refreshingly through their skirts and veils. They gently unstrapped Caleb and situated him comfortably under a large palm tree. There he was out of danger, and hopefully out of sight. Perhaps no one would taunt him today.

"Marah! Hannah!" Leah voiced her greeting from afar. The girls waved back. Leah hoisted her basket of clothes atop her head and came to join her friends. Soon Judith and Sharon arrived, along with Ruth and Sarah. The girls chatted merrily, and the hard work of washing was nearly done before they realized.

"I'm hungry," noted Sarah. Soon everyone was dispersing to collect the midday meal.

Suddenly Judith grabbed Hannah's arm. "Who's that with Caleb?" she asked.

"I don't know," Hannah said. She and Marah abruptly arose and went protectively to their brother.

Seated next to him was a handsome, wavy-haired youth whom they had never seen before. "Hello?" Marah said, a question in her voice.

The boy stood up politely. "Hello," he said with a warm smile that put the girls instantly at ease. "Your brother was just telling me how much he loves it here."

The boy acted as if Caleb were normal. He wasn't bothered by his drooling or his jerking movements. No one had ever acted this way toward Caleb.

Hannah looked skeptical. "You actually understand him?" she asked.

"Yes, when I concentrate and listen carefully enough," admitted the boy. "We were having quite a conversation."

Caleb actually smiled. His whole being seemed transformed. Marah noticed and motioned to Hannah. "I can't believe it," Hannah whispered.

They stood in awkward silence. Then Hannah said, "We're ready to eat. Will you join us?"

"Yes," said the boy, detaching a meal pouch from his waist.

Marah unpacked the lunches she had made and set them on a cloth in front of them. At that moment, a tattered beggar approached.

"They always know when it's lunchtime," Hannah said with annoyance.

"Just ignore him," whispered Marah, adjusting her veil to hide her face.

The boy seemed not to hear. "Are you hungry?" he asked the man. The man nodded furiously.

"Here," offered the boy, "take this." The man nodded again. He grabbed the boy's lunch pouch violently as if he were afraid it would disappear. Marah and Hannah gaped in disbelief.

"And here," the boy said after unstrapping his sandals. "Your feet are cut and painful. These sandals will help protect them."

The beggar, grateful beyond words, took the sandals and shuffled away, sobbing so hard his entire body shook.

"Won't you be hungry now?" asked Marah, who had packed barely enough food for Hannah, Caleb, and herself.

"Not on bread alone does man live," the boy replied mysteriously.

"What does that mean?" puzzled Marah.

"I will feed myself on thoughts of joy, knowing that the poor beggar will not go hungry today," the boy answered.

"And your sandals! They looked brand new! How could you just give them away?" Hannah was appalled.

The boy smiled kindly. "He needs them much more than I."

Hannah and Marah shook their heads.

Instantly, a cloud of dust arose just feet away, distracting all of them. Jonas and Nathan were locked fiercely together in a fight. They grappled savagely. Bruised and bleeding, they tumbled headlong over each other and onto rocks.

Other boys, lead by Zed and Matthew, encouraged the battle. "Give him what he deserves! Kick him!" they screamed, forming a circle around the two opponents.

Marah and Hannah's new acquaintance arose calmly from his place. He strode over, broke the circle, and approached the opponents. With a strength that surprised everyone, he separated them and said, "There are other ways to settle things. Go, talk." The boys, panting with relief, stood staring.

Zed was wild with rage. Gnarling his fists, he challenged the peace-making boy. "Come on," he goaded. He slapped the boy's face. The boy bravely stood his ground with his hands at his sides, matching his will against Zed's anger. Zed gave in, stalking away.

The other boy started toward home. Stares and murmurs followed him.

Matthew said sarcastically, "Who does he think he is, somebody's savior or something?"

"Actually, I think he's quite remarkable," said Marah.

It was then that Hannah noticed he was leaving. The sun outlined his form, casting a radiance around him as he walked. "Wait!" she called loudly. "What's your name?"

The boy turned around and gave a friendly wave. "Jesus," he replied and continued on his uphill climb.

WHO WILL EVER KNOW?

by John H. Marshall

It was the week of the great feast of Passover and was Jeremy ever excited. It meant no school and plenty of free time for him to make good use of his new boat. He'd received the little row boat as a gift from his parents on his eleventh birthday, which was just a few days past. In fact, that's what he and his little dog, Flek, were doing right now. They were about ready to put the boat into the water, when Jeremy was distracted by something he saw going on across the lake.

"I wonder what they're all up to, Flek?" he said, as the two of them looked out across the choppy blue water. On the far side, they could see there were gathered hundreds, perhaps even thousands, of people.

"Yip! Yap!" answered Flek. ("Flek," in the Jewish language, means, "spot" and the little dog certainly was true to his name. He had so many spots that no one could really tell if he was white with black spots, or black with white spots.)

"Come on, boy! Let's go see what is happening!" Jeremy cried, then hopped into the boat with Flek right at his heels.

The lake they were about to cross was near the city of Capernaum, in the country of Samaria. It was a very pretty lake and it was kept full of water by the Jordan River, which flowed into its upper end. All around the lake was also very beautiful. There were green terraces which were covered with olive trees, fig trees and many vineyards. Also, there were lots and lots of palm trees which whispered in the warm, gentle breeze that drifted across the Sea of Galilee, not far from there.

The lake was about half a mile wide at that point, and after they were about midway, Jeremy said as he tugged at the oars, "Not too much farther to go now, Flek!"

"Yip, Yap!" said Flek, wagging his short tail.

"You silly dog," Jeremy said, then rested a bit.

Jeremy could see that the crowd of people had grown even larger, and with more and more coming. This made him even more curious. He quickly grabbed up the oars and paddled even harder than before. In addition to wanting to satisfy his curiosity, he knew that it was getting late in the day and he'd promised his mom to be home before dark.

After much hard paddling (with absolutely no help from Flek) the two finally reached the other shore, not far from where the large crowd was gathered.

After pulling his boat high up on the bank, safe from the waves, Jeremy and Flek headed toward the crowd. Suddenly, Jeremy came to an abrupt halt.

"We forgot our supper, Flek! Why didn't you remind me?" Jeremy said, then turned and went back to the boat.

"Yip! Yap!" said Flek.

Jeremy quickly retrieved his food basket from the boat, then they were both off and running.

That morning, Jeremy's mom had made some unleavened (meaning non-rising, or made without yeast) barley biscuits. Jeremy told his mom he and Flek were going on an outing that afternoon, so she put seven of the small biscuits, along with three salted fish, in his basket. It would be Jeremy and Flek's supper.

When Jeremy and Flek arrived at the edge of the crowd, Jeremy could hear the far-off voice of someone speaking. The voice was coming from somewhere up front.

"Wonder who he is, Flek? Do you suppose it could be the holy prophet? The one they call John the Baptist?" (News traveled very slowly in those days, and Jeremy hadn't heard that evil King Herod already had John the Baptist killed.)

It appeared quite impossible for them to make their way into the crowd, so after Jeremy had some chin-rubbing thoughts on the matter, he said, "I got it! We'll climb high above them—up there behind where the man is talking. That way we can sit down and have our supper while we're listening to whatever it is he has to say. Come on, boy!"

"Yip! Yap!" answered Flek and the two of them began making their way around the crowd and up the terraced embankment.

It took them quite some time to reach their destination, but they finally did. They had gotten quite close and directly over the front of the crowd, but by this time, the man had apparently finished talking.

"Oh me, the story of my life, 'A minute late and a denarius short'," Jeremy moaned. It was a favorite saying of his father and Jeremy liked repeating his funny sayings.

"Well, at least we can have our supper now," Jeremy said, as he squatted down on the ground and removed the cloth which covered the food basket. He then took one small barley biscuit and gave it to Flek. After this, he took a biscuit for himself, plus a salted fish. Flek didn't like fish.

As he munched on his fish and biscuit, Jeremy could hear the group of thirteen men (he'd counted them) talking below him. His attention was on one man in particular; the one who had been talking to the crowd.

As he looked at the man, something very strange and unusual seemed to come over Jeremy. He couldn't explain it, but it seemed to fill him up with a wondrous and beautiful feeling. It was a feeling which Jeremy hoped would never, ever leave him.

His mind was so engrossed with the man that he was unaware of anything around him. Until, that is, he was suddenly startled back into awareness. He realized that someone was standing directly over Flek and him.

"Yip! Yap!" barked Flek, as Jeremy looked up to see who it was. He quickly saw that it wasn't the leader, but one of the other twelve he'd seen. The man had a very kind face and Jeremy wasn't a bit frightened.

"Hello, young man," the stranger said in a deep voice.

"Hi," said Jeremy in a slightly nervous voice.

"I see you're having your supper," said the stranger.

"Yes, sir," Jeremy said, holding out a barley biscuit to the man.

"What's your name?" the man said, not taking the biscuit.

"Jeremy. What's yours?"

"I'm called Simon Peter," the man said, then kneeled down beside Jeremy and Flek.

"This is Flek," Jeremy said as he watched Simon Peter carefully.

"Hello, Flek," Simon Peter said as he rubbed the top of Flek's head. Flek, usually shy with strangers, seemed to like Simon Peter.

Still rubbing Flek, Simon Peter spoke and said, "Jeremy, this may sound like a strange and unusual request, but I would like to borrow your supper for a little while."

Borrow my supper? How can anybody do that? And why? Jeremy thought, but seeming not to have much control over his own words, said, "Yes, sir," and then handed over the basket with the five remaining biscuits and two fish.

"Neither this act of kindness, nor you, Jeremy, will ever be forgotten," Simon Peter said. He quickly stood up and left, heading down the hill toward the others.

After a few dazed moments, Jeremy realized he'd totally forgotten to ask Simon Peter the name of the man who was the leader. At the same time he also realized it was almost dark. Jumping up from the ground, he cried, "Come on, Flek! Mom's going to tan my hide!" After which, they scurried down the hill and were soon back at their boat.

It was not until they were halfway across the lake that Jeremy looked back. When he did, he was quite surprised to see that all the people in the huge crowd seemed to be sitting down and they were eating. "Simon Peter must have been the only one who forgot to bring along his supper," Jeremy muttered.

In spite of having only one small biscuit and tiny fish, Jeremy didn't feel a bit hungry. In fact, he seemed to be very, very full inside. Just as though he'd eaten a feast.

"Maybe I better not tell Mom I let someone borrow my supper and my food basket," he said to Flek, "She might get mad. And besides, what's that Dad is always saying? Something about who will know or care a hundred years from now?

"Yeah, that's it. A hundred years from now, who'll ever know anything about all this, boy?"

"Yip! Yap!" said Flek.

THE SPARROW

by Marion Schoeberlein

The little bird saw Jesus praying in the garden. It was a beautiful garden called Gethsemane.

He is sweating great drops of blood, the bird thought, and they are falling to the ground.

He did not know the man's name was Jesus, but he knew there was something extraordinary about Him.

I wonder who those men are sleeping near Him, the sparrow thought, as it flew to another tree over their heads.

They were Jesus' disciples.

The garden got darker and darker. But the darkness was like silk and velvet.

Suddenly the sparrow heard a rustling noise. Then he saw a radiant light.

"What is that?" the bird asked himself. "Can it be another bird?"

But it was not another bird. It was an angel. The little bird watched the shining, white angel touch Jesus' folded hands and his sweating brow.

He seemed stronger now. Ready for anything, even death on a cross.

Now Jesus was praying out loud and the sparrow heard him say, "Father, if thou be willing, remove this cup from me; nevertheless not my will, but thine, be done."

Then He got up and went over to His disciples. He woke them up.

Sleepyheads! And at such a time! the little bird thought.

In the distance he saw a man with a curly, black beard. He was leading some men who carried torches.

It was Judas, the disciple who was going to betray Him.

"Run away, run away!" the sparrow chirped. He did not like the look in this man's eyes.

But Jesus did not run away. He only stood there.

Judas came forward and kissed Jesus.

Then the sparrow heard Jesus say, "Judas, betrayest thou the Son of Man with a kiss?"

Now the men were leading Jesus away into the darkness and the little bird watched until He was only a speck in the distance.

The garden was very still.

The darkness was so big and the sparrow was so very small.

He let out a wild chirp. The chirp was his song and it meant that he was very sad.

It was his prayer to the God of all the sparrows on this earth.

"Oh, Lord, You will die for us, too!" were the words of his prayer.

And the Garden of Gethsemane echoed with the sadness of the little bird.

His eye was on the sparrow.

IN THE BEGINNING

by Ken Jelmeland

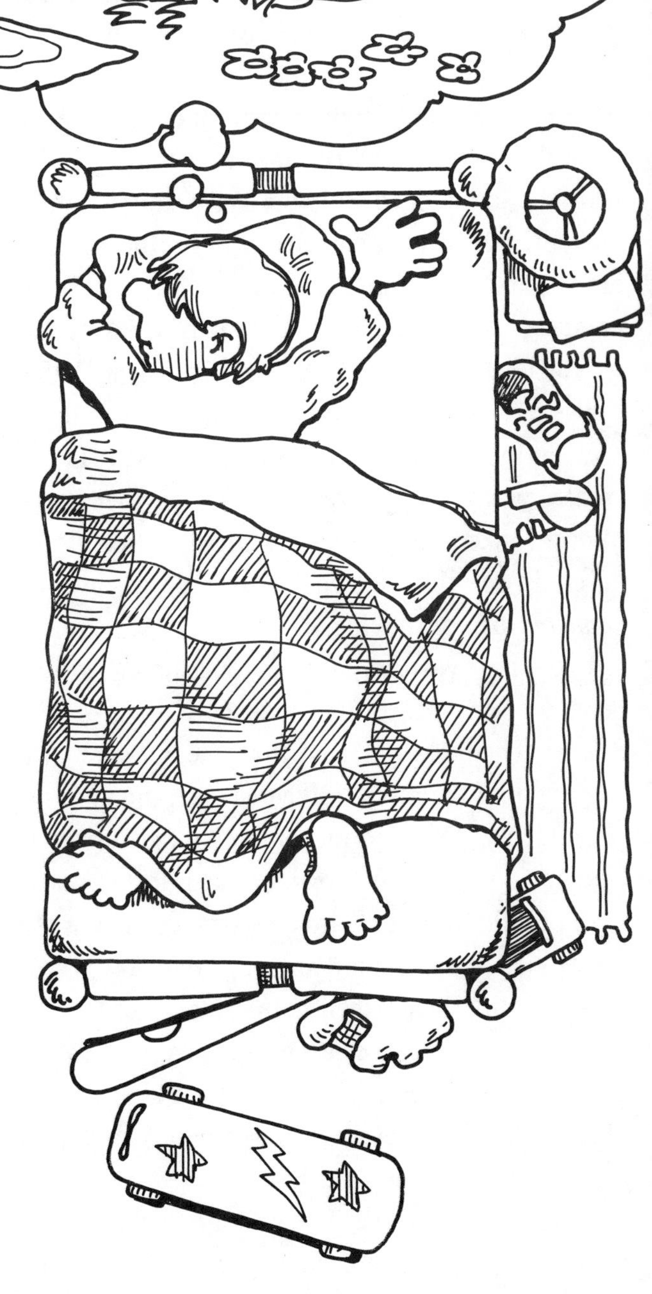

"And that, Harold, is the story of how God created Adam and Eve, and how the first sin happened," said his father as he quietly closed his Bible.

"ZZZZZ . . ." snored Harold in reply, as he rolled to the other side of his warm comfortable bed.

Harold's father wondered if Harold had heard any of the story about Adam and Eve, or whether he had slept through all of it. Harold liked to sleep almost as much as he liked to eat. This was probably why Harold, at age ten, was larger than most of the twelve-year-old boys in his school. But Harold's father shouldn't have worried, because God had something special for Harold that night.

Harold began to dream. Suddenly, he found himself in the middle of the most beautiful garden he had ever seen. Warm sunshine flowed through the gently moving branches of many tall trees. Harold could feel the grass tickling his bare feet. He could smell the thousands of beautiful flowers that decorated the garden everywhere that he looked.

Harold yawned and began to think that this was probably the greatest place he would ever find to take a nap. Of course Harold didn't realize this was only a dream. It seemed so real!

But just as Harold was about to lie down in

a soft, shaded place under one of the trees, he realized there was someone else in the garden with him.

At least He looked like a man. But not just a man. He was someone far greater than any man could ever be. Harold, although he thought and thought, could never really describe Him. You might think that Harold was afraid, but Harold had never felt more loved than he did at that moment. He felt very, very small, but at the same time he felt that he was important.

As Harold watched, the One with him in the garden began to make something from the earth. He began to mold two feet, then legs, and then the rest of a man's body. Harold moved closer as He fashioned a face from the dirt of the ground. Harold had watched sculptors make statues before, but he had never seen such a beautiful work of art. Everything about the man who was being created was perfect, and the Creator obviously loved what He was doing. It looked like He felt that it was the most important thing He had ever done.

Soon the Creator was finished. The man He had created was perfect in every way. The earthen statue almost looked alive. But, as Harold moved closer, he could see that he was only made of dirt. He was not alive or moving.

But what was the Creator doing now? He was bending over the statue's face as if to give him a kiss. Then Harold saw that the Creator was blowing into the mouth of the earthen man.

Suddenly, the coloring of the statue began to change from the soft brown of earth to the warm pink of human flesh. Harold saw movement as the statue's chest began to move up and down with each breath. The earthen statue was alive!

The Creator watched expectantly as His creation opened his eyes. Harold thought they looked a lot like the Creator's eyes. It was obvious that they loved each other very much.

Harold watched as the new man stood up and began to walk around, looking with wonder and surprise at all of the beautiful things in the garden.

Harold was a little embarrassed at first, because the man didn't have any clothes on. But no one else seemed to mind, so Harold decided that it was okay.

Then, the Creator called to the man. He called him Adam. He told Adam that the garden was for him, and that he could eat of any of the fruit in the garden except for one. That one was the fruit from the tree of the knowledge of good and evil.

Harold watched then, as all the animals began to walk past Adam. He gave names to all of them, such as: elephants, foxes, giraffes, eagles, cows, caterpillars, lions. There was a male and a female of each kind of animal and each kind of animal was different from the other.

As the animals paraded past Adam, Harold noticed something. Adam looked sad. He heard Adam ask the Creator why each of the animals had a mate but he had not seen anyone like himself.

The Creator answered by putting Adam into a very deep sleep. Harold thought Adam was dead at first, but then he saw that he was still breathing. Then, to Harold's surprise, he saw the Creator reach His hand into Adam's side and bring out one of Adam's ribs. Harold cringed a little because he didn't like to see blood. But the place where it had come from immediately healed. It was a miracle!

Harold watched with great amazement as the Creator began to mold the rib as He had molded the dirt into Adam. First there were feet, then legs. This time it wasn't a man, it was a woman.

Harold was surprised to hear Adam's voice again. He was saying, "You shall be called woman, because you have been taken out of man." Then Adam called her Eve, and as Harold looked, he saw Adam looking at Eve in that special way that his Mom and Dad looked at each other. It was time for him to leave them alone.

So, Harold turned and walked slowly in the other direction. He decided a little exploring would be fun and interesting, especially since it was starting to get dark. Soon Harold found a comfortable, soft bed of leaves, sheltered among a large grove of trees. After eating some of the delicious fruit that was everywhere, he lay down on the soft bed of leaves, looking forward to some much-needed sleep. But Harold didn't sleep right away. He began to feel very lonely. Everything seemed so real. Was this really a dream?

Suddenly, Harold heard a rustling in the bushes beside him. Harold was afraid. But as he turned, he saw the most beautiful creature that he had ever seen. He would have said that it was a serpent, but it didn't look at all like other serpents that he had seen. It made Harold feel a little strange and cold inside.

Harold went exploring again. Boy, this dream was so realistic! He moved toward the voices that he could hear a short distance away. It was a woman's voice, and a beautiful, almost musical, voice that was unlike anything Harold had ever heard before.

The woman was saying, "But the Creator has said we may eat of the fruit of the trees in the garden, except for the fruit of the tree which is in the middle of the garden, the tree of the knowledge of good and evil. We are not to eat from it or even touch it or we will die."

As Harold moved through a last small group of bushes he saw the beautiful creature that he had seen the night before, and the woman was standing by it. It was sly as it spoke to the woman, "You will not die, for the Creator knows that if you eat of its fruit your eyes will be opened and you will be like Him, knowing both good and evil." Harold's eyes wandered to the most beautiful tree that he had ever seen. It was planted there in the center of the garden. His mouth began to water and his stomach began to growl as he looked at the scrumptious fruit hanging on that tree. Harold watched as the woman's hand reached slowly for a piece of fruit on the forbidden tree, then slowly took a bite.

Something was wrong! Adam, who had been standing close by, but just behind a bush where Harold couldn't see him, rushed up to Eve shouting, "What have you done?"

"The serpent made me eat," said Eve as she handed some of the fruit to Adam.

Harold watched as Adam slowly brought the fruit to his mouth and ate too. But Adam's eyes were sad beyond hope. It was like he knew Eve was going to die and he couldn't bear to be without her.

Suddenly, both Adam and Eve turned red with embarrassment and ran off to cover their nakedness.

Harold looked for the serpent. It was nowhere to be seen. He sat down and a terrible sense of wrongness filled his thoughts. In the distance he could hear the Creator calling for Adam and Eve. The Creator's voice was very firm, "Eve, you will birth your children in much pain, your desire will be for your husband, and he will rule over you." "Adam, because you have listened to your wife and eaten from the tree that I commanded you not to eat from, the ground will be cursed and you shall work for all you receive from it the rest of your life. It will grow thorns and thistles, and when you die you shall return to the ground from which you were taken."

Harold began to cry as he saw the Creator send Adam and Eve away from the garden. The last thing he remembered before waking up was the awesome cherubim with a flaming sword that the Creator placed at the entrance of the garden to guard the Tree of Life.

The shrill buzz of the alarm clock was even more horrible than usual to Harold's ears. The sun was brightly shining through his window, but there was no joy in his heart. In fact, both his pillow and his pajamas were wet from his tears.

What a dream, thought Harold! It seemed so real!

VOICE IN THE NIGHT

by K. H. Munn

"Samuel, Samuel," came the voice in the night.

Sam jumped out of bed. "Yes, sir, you called me?" he said as he ran into Eli's room.

Eli was the boss priest of the people of Israel and Sam was his helper. Samuel's mother, Hannah, had not been able to have a baby, so she promised God that if He gave her a son, she would dedicate him to work in the temple for all his life. God did that, so Sam's mother took him along to the temple to work for the Lord as soon as he was able to live without the milk that her body provided for him.

Sam had been working for the priest, Eli, for quite a while when, in the dark of night, he heard a voice speaking to him. "Samuel, Samuel," said the voice.

Sam and Eli slept in separate rooms of the temple. It was just a tent because the people of Israel were still wandering in the desert, but large enough that it had two rooms. Samuel was resting in the most holy room of the temple. "You called me, sir?" he asked, as he ran into Eli's room.

Eli was puzzled. "No, Son, I didn't call you. Go back to bed," he said. So Sam did.

"Samuel, Samuel," he heard again! He ran again into Eli's room to see what he wanted but was again sent back to bed. This happened three times before Eli realized what was happening.

The third time Eli told him, "Go back to bed, Son, and the next time you hear the voice calling, say, 'Speak, Lord, for your servant is listening.' "

Sam did that, even though he was feeling pretty crabby about being bothered while he was trying to sleep. God told him that Eli's sons had sinned against Him and would not be permitted to live, and neither would any future man in Eli's family! This was because they held themselves above the rest of the people and demanded special favors. The next morning Eli asked Sam what God had said to him, so Samuel told him, even though he was afraid. The sons were priests too, because of Eli, and because they belonged to the priestly family. The family came down through Moses' brother, Aaron, who was the first priest. This made it dangerous because priests were very important in those days, but Sam did as he was told.

"He is the Lord, let Him do what is good in His eyes," was all Eli said. Samuel was very glad and grateful to Eli.

That's what happened, except that God came to Samuel many times in the days to come, too, and told him that he would be the boss priest himself, a leader of Israel.

And it certainly was true, Samuel did become a great leader of the tribe of Israel.

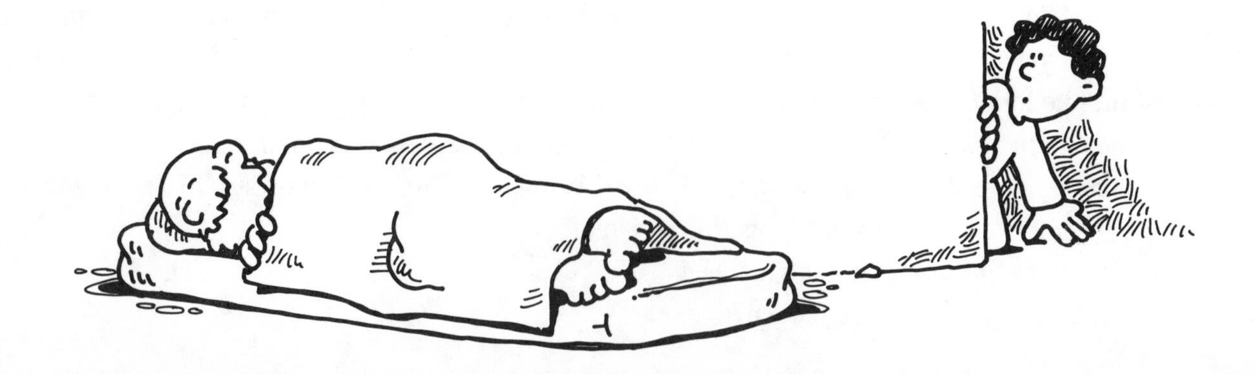

THE HARP

by Marion Schoeberlein

Jabal loved helping his father tend the sheep. He loved walking in the soft, green hills of summer.

Sometimes he was so happy he couldn't keep from singing.

Nahan, his father, was a very practical man. "Keep your mind on the flock, Son," he scolded, "I think you sing because that boy David has an influence over you."

There was no doubt about it. David did influence him.

"I love the way he plays his harp, Father," Jabal defended his friend, "he's already making up little psalms to go with his music."

"He's more of a psalm-singer than he is a shepherd," Nahan said, "and I don't want you to spend so much time with him."

Jabal said no more about it. He knew his father's mind was made up, and it was useless to try to change his mind.

Whenever his father left him alone with the sheep, and he heard the sound of David's golden harp, he followed the sound like a child into the Pied Piper's hill.

It was a game David and he played.

"You're just like an older brother to me," Jabal told him. "Where do the words come from in your psalms?"

David smiled. It flattered his ego that Jabal doted on him. He was not used to so much honor at home.

"I just make up the words as they come to me," he said, "the Lord sends them to me. Do you want to hear the one I made up yesterday?"

Jabal nodded.

"The Lord is my shepherd; I shall not want. He maketh me to lie down in green pastures: he leadeth me beside the still waters. He restoreth my soul: he leadeth me in the paths of righteousness for his name's sake.

Yea, though I walk through the valley of the shadow of death, I will fear no evil: for thou art with me; thy rod and thy staff they comfort me."

"I do not understand it all," Jabal said, "but it is very beautiful."

"I did not finish it, though," David said, "I want to add some verses to it."

Then he began strumming his harp again and the golden tinkle of the notes echoed through the hills.

"Do you think I could ever make music like you do, David?" Jabal asked.

"Someday, I think you will. I have a secret to tell you. Someday soon I will give you the harp and then you will learn it."

"But why are you giving me your wonderful instrument?" Jabal was very curious now.

"Because the prophet Samuel came to annoint me as the future King of Israel. Think of it, Jabal, me, a shepherd boy, with a destiny. Samuel said it was the will of God."

Jabal thought David must feel as if he stood on a mountain instead of these Bethlehem hills. His thoughts must be reaching the stars and touching them.

"I am so happy for you, David," Jabal threw his arms around his friend. "May I strum the harp just once today?"

David put the harp into his hands. "It's easy," he said, "just touch it lightly once."

Jabal touched it and happy notes ascended, each one a little prayer.

"When I am king I will have all the harps I want," David said, "but I will always remember that I gave you my first one. Promise me that you will make happy sounds on it forever."

"I promise," said Jabal as he handed the harp back to its owner.

"Now I know the verses I will add to my psalm," David said, "listen and I will sing them to you."

"Thou preparest a table before me in the presence of mine enemies: thou anointest my head with oil; my cup runneth over. Surely goodness and mercy shall follow me all the days of my life: and I will dwell in the house of the Lord for ever."

"It is a psalm for a king," Jabal said.

"No, it is only the psalm of a poor shepherd boy who will be king someday. I must return home now to my father. Remember, it is our secret. And remember, too, that the harp will be yours."

How could I forget? Jabal thought. Today he had been blessed with a secret, a psalm and a harp. His life was like music now.

THE FRIENDS' FAITH

A WEE MOUSE ADVENTURE
by Anne Evans

Four men were talking very seriously. "He's our friend," said one. "We must help him."

"Remember all he did for us when he was well and strong. Now that he's helpless we should not forget him," said another.

But how can we take him to the Savior," said a third. "He is too heavy for one person to carry. And once we get there, where would we put him; he's in his bed all the time."

"That's easy," said the first man, "we'll let him stay on his mattress and each one of us will take a corner and we'll carry him to Capernaum where the Savior is staying."

The four men went to the man who was crippled with palsy and told him of their plan to help him.

Wee Mouse sat in the corner listening. How great of these four men to take their friend to see Jesus. They had faith that Jesus could cure their friend.

The paralyzed man lay back on his mattress, tears of thanks in his eyes. "Thank you, my friends," he said. "I know if I can see the Savior I will be cured. I will be well again. You shall see."

And so the four men each picked up a corner of the mattress and carried the man to Capernaum.

The hot sun beat down upon them as they went and Wee Mouse ran along with them, anxious to see Jesus cure the sick man.

"Can you tell us where to find the Savior?" they asked.

"Yes," said a man. "He is staying at the end of the road. You will find Him surrounded by people."

It was a large house made of soft, baked bricks, with a stairway that led to the flat roof made of branches and clay.

"Oh, no!" cried Wee Mouse when she ran up to the house. "There are so many people here, the men will never be able to bring their friend to see Jesus." And indeed, the house was overflowing. There were people in every room, and they were even spilling out into the courtyard, packed like a herd of sheep.

Wee Mouse ran round and round nipping at people's feet, trying to get them to step aside to clear a pathway to Jesus so the men could bring their friend to Him. But no one would step aside, they only crowded closer, anxious to hear every word that Jesus said.

The men looked down at the packed house. "We will never get in," they said. "Perhaps we never should have come."

"Do not lose your faith," said the first man. "Surely there must be some way we can take our friend to the Savior so he can be cured."

Wee Mouse came out of the house, for if she stayed inside, she surely would be stepped on. She ran round and round the house to see if there were other openings through which the friends could take the man. But all the openings were filled with people. She ran up the stairs to the flat roof, but no opening could she find there either.

She was so discouraged, she just sat there thinking, when suddenly she saw something moving. It was a line of ants moving. It was a line of ants coming out of a crack in the roof.

The crack ran deep and narrow. Wee Mouse peeked down and could see a shaft of light as the sun shone in the windows of the room below. Then she had an idea! If only the men would come up on the roof. But first she had to do something.

She started to scratch at the tiny crack, and she scratched and she scratched until the crack became large enough for someone to take notice of it.

"There," she said. "It is ready."

But when she came back to the men, they were getting ready to take their sick friend back home. They were discouraged.

"No! No!" squeaked Wee Mouse. "Come up on the roof. Come up on the roof!" And she tugged at the first man's robe, trying to make him stay. But the man just shook his robe and shook Wee Mouse off.

Then he said to the others, "Before we go back, let me check again to see if there is some other door or entrance one can go in to see the Savior."

Wee Mouse ran around with him, knowing he wouldn't find anything, but the man was determined, and after he came back to the front of the house he stood by the stairs. "I may as well check the roof," he said. "It can do no harm."

So he climbed the steep stairs up to the flat roof and looked around. "Nothing here," he muttered, as he looked up and down.

Just then, his eye fell upon the crack in the roof. "What's this," he exclaimed as he stooped to inspect the crack. Suddenly, a broad grin spread over his face.

"That's it!" he cried, as he bent over the crack. "The roof is cracked. It will be easy to cut a hole in the roof. There's more than one way to get into this house to see the Savior. We will follow the crack and cut a hole in the roof. The rest will be simple."

Wee Mouse watched.

And so they carried the paralyzed man up to the roof.

"Once we cut a hole in the roof," said the friends, "how are we going to get him to Jesus?"

"That's easy," said the man. "I will get some rope and we'll slide it under the mattress and lower him down."

And so they cut a hole in the roof and lowered the man down to Jesus' feet.

Jesus looked up and saw the four men peeping through the hole in the roof, their faces full of hope.

"Master; we have faith that you can cure our friend," they said.

And when Jesus saw their faith he said to the paralyzed man,"My son, your sins are forgiven."

Now there were certain enemies of Jesus in the crowd, and they said, "How can this son of man say, 'Your sins are forgiven', when only God can forgive sins."

Jesus answered, "Is it easier to say 'Your sins are forgiven,' or say 'Rise up and walk'?" No one would know for sure if the man's sins were forgiven, but they would see if the man could rise up and walk.

Then Jesus laid His hands upon the man and said, "I say to you, rise up, take your mattress and walk home."

And behold, the paralyzed man did rise up, completely cured, and took up his mattress and started home.

"A miracle! A miracle!" cried the crowd.

How happy the friends were, and they laughed with joy.

Wee Mouse was happy too.

THE WEDDING FEAST

A WEE MOUSE ADVENTURE
by Anne Evans

"Have you heard," clucked the hen, "there's going to be a great wedding feast here in Cana. All the important people will be here."

"I know," replied Wee Mouse, "but there will be someone even more important than the bridegroom. Jesus will be there with His disciples. And His mother, Mary, has been invited too. Oh, it will be a fine wedding party."

And Wee Mouse sighed with happiness, thinking of all the crumbs that would be dropped. What a feast she would have! She hurried on to the groom's house where the wedding would be held. Her eyes grew wide with wonder when she saw all the food spread out on the tables, and so much wine! Surely it would be a great feast.

She looked around for a place to hide where no one would see her and chase her away. And soon she spied six huge water jugs stacked up against the wall.

"That's it," squeaked Wee Mouse. "I will hide behind one of the jugs and no one will see me. I'll be able to peek around them and see the whole wedding feast."

Soon the guests arrived in their finest linens and smelling of fragrant spices. And the musicians played sweet music, people danced and were merry.

Everyone crowded around the bride and groom to admire their fine clothes and wish them much happiness and good health. But no one paid much attention to the quiet young man who stood on the edge of the gathering watching all the happy people.

Now and then someone would come up to Him and say, "Aren't you Joseph's son? I remember you when you were a young boy. What a fine young man you've grown to be."

And Jesus' mother, Mary, would hear and her heart swelled with love for her son.

Yes, He had grown to be a fine young man and she was very proud of Him. He was very special.

Wee Mouse heard from behind the water jugs and she felt good. Jesus was a young man now and a few disciples followed Him. People were starting to listen as He told of His heavenly Father and preached love and kindness. And Jesus stood there watching all the happy people.

"More wine! More food!" ordered the host as the guests kept pouring in. Soon it seemed as if the whole town were at the wedding feast. The servants poured more wine and offered more food to the guests, and the guests ate and ate and drank and drank. And one guest having had his fill of sweet cake, put his last mouthful on the edge of the low wall in the garden.

Wee Mouse saw it there. How good it looked, all covered with honey and nuts. It would be a

tasty treat for her. She would get it later.

More wine! More food!" cried the host again.

Wee Mouse was worried. Would they have enough, for surely the host did not plan for this many people. She crept out from behind the water jugs and ran to the room where the wine and food was kept.

"What are we going to do," cried one of the servants in dismay. "The wine is almost gone. There are so many people to be served and there just isn't enough wine. The groom will be so ashamed if he doesn't have enough for the people. Everyone will talk about him and say that he is stingy."

Just then, Jesus' mother entered the room. "Where are the servants with the wine?" she asked. "The guests' glasses are empty and they are asking for more wine."

"There isn't any more," cried the servants. "It is all gone."

Mary sighed, a worried frown wrinkled her brow. Something must be done. They must have more wine. She would go to her son, Jesus. She was sure He could do something about it. She had that much faith in Him.

"See that young man over there," she said to the servants as she pointed to Jesus. "He is my son and He can help you. I will speak to Him and you are to do whatever He says.

The servants shook their heads in doubt. There just wasn't any more wine, and there wasn't anything anyone could do about it.

"Son," said Mary to Jesus, as she went to Him, "the wedding feast has run out of wine. You must do something about it."

"Do something," replied Jesus, "There is nothing I can do. My time has not come to perform miracles. I am not ready." And Jesus sighed and walked out into the garden. He stood by the low stone wall that surrounded the flower beds and His eye fell upon the discarded piece of sweet cake. If only there was as much wine as there was cake. His mother was asking Him to perform a miracle and produce more wine. He had never performed a miracle, yet His mother had faith in Him. Surely His heavenly Father would help Him.

Wee Mouse watched as Jesus stood there, a worried frown upon His face. "You can do it. I know you can," she squeaked. But Jesus did not hear her. He was lost in thought, praying that His heavenly Father would show Him the way.

Moments slipped by. Then, as if by a miracle, the troubled look disappeared from Jesus' face. A new light shown in His eyes. And turning, He strode back to the servants. Wee Mouse followed.

"Fill those jugs with water," He commanded as He pointed to the great jugs that Wee Mouse had hidden behind.

"Do as He says," commanded Mary to the servants. And the doubting servants went to the well and drew water and filled the six great jugs.

Then Jesus blessed the filled jugs and called the host to Him.

"Drink," He said as He handed the host a filled cup. And the host drank.

"Why, this is excellent wine. A miracle! A miracle!" cried the host. "It is even better than the wine we first had."

Wee Mouse was happy and proud. It was Jesus' first miracle. She ran back to the garden wall to find her cake.

THE SOLDIER'S FAITH

A WEE MOUSE ADVENTURE

by Anne Evans

The servant lay upon the bed, shivering and shaking so hard that even the bed shook. Wee Mouse knew that the man was dying of palsy.

Soon the master came into the room. He was a great hulk of a man, dressed in the uniform of a Roman commander. His huge muscles rippled under the shiny arm band as he stretched forth his hand and laid it upon the feverish head of his servant.

"Oh, noble servant," he said, "I am so powerless to help you. You have served me well, and I love you as a son. If only I could do something to make you well again." And great tears fell from his eyes as he looked at his sick servant.

Wee Mouse was worried. She knew the servant was going to die. And she knew that Jesus could cure the servant, for He had performed many miracles, and now He was right here in Capernaum with His disciples. But she knew that the Roman soldier was afraid to ask Jesus to cure his servant, because Jesus was a Jew. And even though the Roman loved Jesus and believed in Him, he couldn't ask Jesus into his house. Jewish laws forbade it. Then too, the Roman army was stationed in Capernaum and had control of the city.

What could Wee Mouse do. If only she could get the Roman soldier to go to Jesus and ask Him to cure his beloved servant. The Roman didn't even know that Jesus was in Capernaum.

Wee Mouse crept out from where she was hiding in a corner of the room. "Follow me," she squeaked as she ran around in circles trying to get the soldier's attention. But the soldier only sat there, his head held in his hands.

Wee Mouse climbed up on the windowsill and she squeaked and she squeaked until finally the soldier looked up.

"A mouse," he said. "A little mouse running around and nothing wrong with it. What good is it to anyone; and yet my faithful servant lies dying with palsy." And going to the window he opened it, saying, "Be off with you, pest. I could crush you with my bare hands, but I have heard of the one they call Jesus, and He preaches love, even to tiny creatures. I believe in Him. I do. He could cure my servant. I know He could.

"Jesus is here," cried Wee Mouse as she jumped from the window. "He is here in Capernaum. Follow me. I will take you to Him."

But the soldier only looked away and pulled the window shut. He didn't understand the squeaks of a mouse. He stood by the window, lost in thought. He wanted so much to help his dying servant, and through the closed window he could hear the muffled cries of the crowd.

"Such a racket," he said. "I must have it quiet here. That noise outside will disturb my servant. And what a crowd of people! What are they doing?"

Wee Mouse just had to get the soldier's attention, for soon Jesus would pass by. She ran back to the room, squeaking and tugging at the soldier's cape.

"You again," he muttered, taking a swat at Wee Mouse as she ran up to the windowsill again.

"Jesus! Jesus!" He heard the faint sound coming through the closed window.

"Jesus," he repeated in a daze. "Jesus is here? Can it be true that I am hearing the crowd calling 'Jesus'? I must see Him; but will He listen to me? He must. He must." And he ran out into the street where Jesus stood surrounded by His disciples and a great crowd of people.

The soldier pushed and shoved until he finally came to the disciples. "I must see your Master," he begged as the crowd pushed closer. "My servant is dying of palsy and I know your Master can cure him."

Andrew looked at the soldier for a moment. "Your face looks familiar," he said. "I have seen you before."

"I . . . I . . ." began the soldier. "I am stationed with the Roman army. No doubt you have seen me before. I am not of your faith, but I know of the miracles your Master has performed. I do believe in Him. I do."

"Yes," replied Andrew. "Now I remember you. You are the man who built the fine synagogue for my people. You have done so much to help the Jews. Wait, I will speak to the Savior." And he laid a hand upon Jesus' arm.

Jesus turned and looked at the soldier, His eyes filled with love, for He had heard what Andrew had said. "What is it?" He asked.

The soldier got down on his knees and touched the hem of Jesus' robe. "Please," he begged. "Please cure my servant. He is dying of palsy and I love him truly. He has been so faithful and good, and has been like a son to me. I know you can cure him. I just know you can."

Andrew turned to John, his voice filled with wonder. "See what a great, powerful man the soldier is; and a Roman too. Yet, see how he humbles himself before the Savior." And John agreed.

Jesus listened. "Take me to your house," He said.

The soldier rose. "No, no. I cannot do that," he said. "I am not worthy for you to do that. All you have to do is command and say the word and it will be done. I know it can be done. I am a centurion and have a hundred men in my command. I say, 'go,' and they go. I say 'come,' and they come. I say to my servant 'do this or that,' and he does. I know a command is obeyed. All you have to do is command and my servant will be well again."

Jesus laid His hand on the centurion's shoulder. "Do you truly believe I can cure your servant without seeing him or even touching him with my hand?"

The centurion's head dropped upon his chest and he lowered his eyes. He looked so humble—this great strong man. "I truly believe," he whispered. "I truly do."

Jesus' face shone with love, and His eyes were soft and tender. He turned to His disciples. "Never," He said, "never have I found such faith in all of Israel."

"Go," He said to the centurion. "Go back to your house. Your faith in me has been fulfilled. Your servant is well."

Wee Mouse ran back to the centurion's house, anxious to see the servant. What happy cries she heard!

"Something wonderful has happened," cried the servant as he got up from his bed. "A miracle has happened. I shake no more! I am well! I am well!"

JESUS LOVES THE CHILDREN

A WEE MOUSE ADVENTURE
by Anne Evans

The boy leaned his crutch against the tree and sat down in its shade. In the distance could be heard the bleat of a lamb as it climbed among the rocks looking for tender young grass. Down below was the village with its flat-topped roofs; here and there young mothers ran around calling to their children.

Wee Mouse crawled up against the trunk of the gnarled tree and watched a green lizard as it scampered about looking for tiny bugs. She felt sorry for the young boy, whose leg was as twisted as the tree, because he could not run and play like other children.

She crawled closer to him. She was not afraid, for the boy was gentle and loving.

"If I could only see Him," muttered the boy as his fingers traced a pattern in the sandy soil. "He could make me well. I know He could. But He seems only to have time for older people."

"No, no." squeaked Wee Mouse. "Jesus loves children. He loves them very much. It's only that the crowds always push the children back. Jesus loves everyone and most of all the children."

And Wee Mouse scampered back to the village.

"Come, children," cried the mothers. "Jesus is coming." And the young mothers gathered up their children to take them to see Jesus.

"Jesus is coming. Jesus is coming," cried the children as they clustered together and climbed the hill to see Jesus and His disciples. And there stood Jesus waiting as the crowd caught up with them. Wee Mouse ran ahead.

"See what a crowd there is," said John impatiently. "Will we ever get any rest?"

"And so many children," replied Peter. "They make so much noise and run about so, kicking up the dust. Such a nuisance. But what can we do? We can't send them away; the mothers would never allow it." And he heaved a great sigh of disgust as the children crowded around Jesus.

John stepped forward. "Come, children; do not bother the Savior," he said, as he shooed the children away.

Jesus turned as he heard these words. His voice was stern as He said to the disciples. "Do not forbid these children to come to me, for only through the innocence and belief of a child can we enter into the kingdom of heaven." And the disciples hung their heads in shame as Jesus said, "Little children, come unto me."

Wee Mouse looked up as the children gathered closer to Jesus, some climbing upon His lap and touching Him. Jesus' eyes were full of love and tenderness as He gathered the children to Him.

"Tell us a story," they begged.

Jesus looked at the children, and His eyes fell upon the young crippled boy who had come down from the hill and stood at the edge of the crowd. The boy leaned upon his crutch and held back, for he was a bit older than the little children, and he felt shy and awkward in the presence of the Savior. He took a step forward and watched, the weight of his crutch resting upon a small round stone.

Wee Mouse waited by his side. She wanted to hear the story.

"I will tell you a story that has a message to it," said Jesus. "It is called a parable. Then you can tell me what it means."

He began, "There once was a farmer and he planted some seeds. And some of the seeds fell by the side of the road and the fowl came and ate them.

"Some fell upon stony places where there wasn't much soil. And for a while, the seeds sprouted and grew. But then the sun dried them up because they had no roots and they withered and died.

"And some seeds fell among the thorns, and the strong thorns grew up and choked out the seeds.

"And then some of the seeds fell on good rich soil, and those seeds grew into healthy plants and multiplied and brought forth good fruit."

Jesus' voice grew soft, and He looked at the children. They had grown still while listening to His words. "What did the story mean?" He gently asked as His eyes searched the crowd looking for an answer.

The children shrugged their shoulders. They liked the part about the seeds growing into healthy plants for the farmer, but that was all they understood. "I know what it means," muttered the boy under his breath, as he leaned heavily upon his crutch.

Wee Mouse heard what the boy said.

"Tell him. Tell him," she squeaked. "Go to Jesus and tell him."

But the boy kept quiet, his shyness overcoming him. There were so many little children around Jesus, and he was so much bigger than they were.

"Doesn't anyone know what the story means?" asked Jesus, with disappointment in His voice.

"Tell Him! Tell Him!" squeaked Wee Mouse again.

But the boy remained silent, an embarrassed flush spreading over his cheeks. He just stood there.

Wee Mouse ran around in circles. She was that upset. If the boy would only speak up, then Jesus would see that he was crippled.

Around and around she ran, scattering pebbles and tiny clouds of dust in her excitement. It was so quiet, and all about was a hush of silence. Everyone was waiting for someone to speak up and tell Jesus what the story meant.

Wee Mouse stopped short as the boy shifted his weight on his crutch, when suddenly the crutch slipped off the stone and onto the ground as the boy tumbled forward.

"Oh! Oh!" cried the boy. "I . . ."

Jesus looked up as the boy picked up his crutch.

"Come here, boy," said Jesus kindly. "I have been watching you." And the boy stepped foward.

Wee Mouse followed, knowing now that the boy would have to speak to Jesus.

"Do you know what the story means?" asked Jesus.

The boy took a deep breath. "Yes, I do," he replied. "The seeds are like the Word of God, and Your teachings spread among the people, and God is the farmer. And the rocky soil and thorns were the kind of people who didn't have enough faith and were not strong, so the Word of God did not take root and make people strong and believe. And the seeds, or words of God that were sown in the good soil was sown among people who were good and loving believers. They taught their children and their children's children to be good and believe."

The boy took another deep breath. He had never said so many words to one person before; and here he was saying them to Jesus.

Wee Mouse heaved a happy sigh. She was so proud of the boy.

Jesus stretched forth His hand and touched the boy. "Blessings upon you," He said. "You knew."

And the boy stood straight and tall. His crutch lay on the ground. His twisted leg was whole. He needed the crutch no longer.

Wee Mouse joined the happy group of children as Jesus blessed them.

THE MIRACLE WORKER

by Helen Friesen

"Andrew, it's going to be a nice day. Why don't you take the goats to find some better grazing down by the pasture. Take Jonathan along, too."

"All right, Mother, but can we take a lunch along?" asked Andrew.

"Yes, if you fix it yourself," Mother added in a tired tone of voice. "I have to go help your father fix those nets he tore while fishing yesterday. There's some bread and some cheese. Watch out. I just sharpened that knife yesterday so don't cut yourself. Better take along a goatskin with water, too."

Andrew hurried to the kitchen, found the goatskin, and after cutting some thick slices of bread and cheese, he wrapped it in a clean cloth and put it in a knapsack. Grabbing the goatskin he called, "Come on, Jonathan. Let's walk to the well to fill this before we get the goats."

Jonathan stood up, reached out his hand and Andrew took it. Andrew pushed aside the small stool so Jonathan wouldn't stumble over it while he grabbed his cane.

Outside Jonathan asked, "The sun is shining, isn't it?"

Andrew smiled. He was used to having Jonathan know things that you wouldn't think a blind person knew. "I know," Andrew chuckled. "You feel the warm sun on your head."

Andrew filled the goatskin with water. The cold water would feel good as the day got warmer.

He handed Jonathan the tether of one of the goats while he took the other two as they headed for the meadow. The goats pulled eagerly, sensing their destination.

As they made their way down the path, Andrew saw a group of boys coming from the village. This looked like trouble. Those bullies always teased Jonathan because he was blind. He hated to think what they would say. Jonathan was always kind and gentle.

When Jehu, the leader, spotted the two with their threesome of goats, he pointed at them. Andrew noticed they detoured to come their way.

"Good morning, Andrew," began Jehu with a sneer. "You taking four goats out to pasture?"

Andrew felt the tension mount as he answered in a low voice, "Leave us alone." He noticed Jonathan's face stayed unruffled as he clung tightly to his goat who tugged to get to where he could graze.

Elihu, one of the gang, reached over and grabbed the tether from Jonathan who wasn't expecting it. Elihu startled the goat, let loose of the tether and the goat raced up the path; its bell jangling loudly. The gang just laughed.

Andrew was furious, but he dared not let loose of his ropes to charge the bullies for then both his goats would escape. Andrew tried to guide Jonathan around the boys, but one of the boys stuck out his foot so Jonathan tripped and fell.

That did it. Andrew lashed out with his foot to kick his nearest tormentor. Just then one of the boys hit Andrew's goats with his rod. The unexpected jerk on his tether was enough to pull him to the ground, mashing the bread in his knapsack. The big boys hooted with laughter as they turned and hurried away.

Andrew's face flushed over the insult and he looked to see how Jonathan was. A trickle of blood traced a track down his forehead. He'd struck a rock as he fell. Andrew used the underside of his tunic to wipe away the blood.

"Wait here, Jonathan. I must catch those goats before they get out of sight. I'll come back as soon as I can."

"I'll be all right," assured Jonathan as he wiped more blood away.

Andrew hurried after the goats. The white one had settled down to graze while the other two kept running, dragging their tethers.

The goats headed straight for a group of men coming this way. Seeing Andrew in pursuit of the runaway goats, several of the men understood his problem. The big burly man caught one of the loose tethers while a shorter man quickly caught the other one. They came toward Andrew as he slowed to catch his breath.

The leader of the group asked, "My son, are these your goats?"

"Yes, sir, and I thank you for stopping them." Before he knew it, he was telling about his encounter with the town bullies and how they'd mistreated Jonathan.

"How can they be so mean to him? He wouldn't hurt anyone," Andrew bristled.

"Is that Jonathan sitting over there?" asked the leader.

"Yes. He couldn't help. He's blind so I help him at times even though he's bigger than me, but he knows lots of things. He can tell by the sound of the footsteps who's coming to our house." Andrew said proudly.

While they were walking, the leader asked him his name.

"Andrew, sir."

The leader turned to the shorter man who had caught one of the goats and now had gotten the last of the trio in hand. "See, Andrew, you have a namesake. This boy's name is Andrew too. Let's go meet your brother, Andrew."

Jonathan heard their approach. Andrew yelled, "I got them all, Jonathan. Come meet my new friends. They helped me catch the goats. What's your name, sir?"

"My name is Jesus. Let me look at you, Jonathan. How long have you been blind?"

"I was born blind, sir," replied Jonathan.

Gently Jesus touched his face and asked, "Would you like to see, my son?"

"Very much, sir," Jonathan spoke wistfully.

Andrew watched as Jesus touched Jonathan's eyes, saw his eyelids flutter, blink and squint as though reacting to bright light.

"What's happening?" stammered Andrew.

"I . . . I can see," marveled Jonathan.

"Trees, the sky, the lake, even you!" Then he hurled his cane as far as possible. "Oh, thank you," he cried as he kissed the hand of Jesus.

The men smiled and patted him on the back. Andrew stood in stunned silence. Jonathan said, "I must go home. They'll never believe this."

"Go ahead, Jonathan. I'll bring the goats." Turning to Jesus, Andrew said, "My parents will surely want to thank you. Can you stop a bit?"

"We still have miles to go. Shalom. God bless you and also Jonathan," said Jesus, as he went down the path with his disciples.

Andrew pulled the goats faster than they wanted to go as he tried to catch Jonathan. Since no one was in the house, he saw Jonathan race to the lake.

Andrew saw his mother's amazement as she watched Jonathan hurrying to the dock. Jonathan yelled, "I can see, I can see!"

She dropped her net and ran to meet him, hugging him while tears chased down her cheeks.

"A miracle! Amazing! Who did this?" she demanded.

"A man called Jesus touched my eyes and I could see," said Jonathan.

Turning to her husband she insisted, "We must thank him, Aaron."

When Andrew caught up with them, he added, "The man Jesus couldn't stay, but his men caught our goats. He was so kind, Mother.

"Now teach me to fix the nets and then I want to go fishing with you, Father," begged Jonathan.

"One thing at a time," his father laughed. They watched as Jonathan looked at his reflection in the quiet lake, as unruffled that afternoon as a bowl of pudding.

"So that's the way I look. I often wondered," mused Jonathan.

That night at supper, the prayers included happiness over the gift of sight for Jonathan and gratitude to a man called Jesus.

FRIENDS AT THE TOWER OF BABEL

by Brenda E. Eads

Sarah ran out into the dusty street. A large crowd of excited people were gathered around a man. He seemed to be shouting something to the crowd.

Sarah pressed closer to hear what he was saying. "I tell you, we are a great people," he cried. "We should build a monument to make our name great."

"What would you have us do?" a voice called from the crowd. The man replied, "Let us make bricks and build a tower that reaches to the heavens. Generations will remember us for building such a tower."

Sarah felt a hand on her arm. It was Ruth, her best friend. "What is he talking about?" she whispered.

"Shh," Sarah said. "My father is speaking."

At the words of Sarah's father, the crowd became silent. "What foolishness is this," he called to the man. "We should worship the Lord our God and build altars to Him, not to ourselves."

Some of the crowd murmured approval at his words. The man shouted again, "Will we allow this one man to deny us our right to greatness? I say we build our tower to the heavens!"

"Yes, yes!" roared the people.

Sarah's father came and led them from there, a few others were leaving too. He shook his head sorrowfully as they heard the wild yells of the people.

"What is wrong, Father?" asked Sarah.

"It is wrong to build a monument to ourselves. We are just humble men. The Lord God deserves our praises, not mere men."

"Are my father and brothers there?" asked Ruth.

"Yes, my child, they are probably making bricks by now," answered Sarah's father.

Sarah and Ruths' eyes met and they clasped cold hands. What would happen now?

The days passed, most of the people were joyously working on the tower. A few, like Sarah's father, stayed completely away. It was exciting for Sarah and Ruth as they watched the great monument go up and up. It was so enormous, they could hardly walk around it. Sloping walks curved around the sides in easy grades. The people could travel to each level with little difficulty.

Sarah burst into the house one day and said excitedly, "Oh, Father, you should see it. The tower is so tall, I'm sure it will soon reach God in His heavens.

Her father rebuked her gently, "My daughter, the tower is not the place you will find God. You will find God only by the giving of sacrifice and listening with your heart to hear God's voice."

"I see, Father," said Sarah, "But it is such a wonder to see the tower being built."

"The people think too well of themselves. I fear great harm will come from this thing." Then he said, "Go and find your friend."

Sarah went and met Ruth. They talked of the tower, as it was the main thing on everyone's mind.

"My father says the tower is evil," Sarah said.

"Mine says it is for good," countered Ruth.

"I believe in my father's judgment." said Sarah quietly.

Ruth became angry, "My father is happy and cheerful. Yours just stays inside praying and scowling at the others who are building. How can you believe he is right?"

"I just do," Sarah said stubbornly.

"Then we can't be friends any more!" shouted Ruth. Sarah watched her run away, then walked sadly inside.

She missed Ruth as the days passed. Still, she stayed loyal to her father. The small group that were against the tower met at Sarah's house. Sarah listened as one man said, "I'm fearful the Lord will punish us."

Sarah thought, Will Ruth be punished? I hope not. She is still my friend, even though she is angry with me.

The next day there was a strange feeling in the air. The majority of the people were celebrating, another section of the tower was done. Sarah wandered through the jostling throng. She dodged around a plump matron and came face to face with Ruth.

"Ruth," Sarah exclaimed, "I'm so glad to see you."

Ruth ducked her head in embarrassment. She looked glad to see Sarah too.

"Can't we still be friends even if our father's don't agree?"

Ruth hesitated, then said, "I guess we can try."

"Friends," said Sarah and held out her hand.

"Friends," said Ruth smiling.

The girls hugged each other and went happily about together for the rest of the day.

Toward evening, the celebration became wild and noisy. Sarah's father found them and told them to go home. He said to Ruth, "Run, find your family, this is no place for you."

As Ruth disappeared into the crowd, Sarah was startled by a loud crack of thunder. Then lightning filled the sky. They watched in horror as a shaft of it forked down and struck the wall of the great tower. It was being torn apart by the storm.

Quickly the laughter and merriment of the crowd turned to screams of fear. The people rushed here and there in the confusion. Then, Sarah heard new sounds. People were talking in words she couldn't understand.

"What is happening?" she cried to her father and clung to his hand.

"I'm afraid this is God's punishment," he said, and they hurried to their home.

Sarah went to bed that night hoping that in the morning the nightmare would be over. When daylight came it was easy to see it wasn't. Masses of people were shouting and gesturing. Most turned away in frustration and disgust. As this went on, some found others they could understand. They formed into small groups.

Sarah had not seen Ruth since they parted that night. She searched for her, but she and her family were nowhere to be found.

Sarah's father soon decided their small group should move elsewhere. This included those who had been against the building of the tower.

They were soon packed and everyone was ready to go. Sarah cast a last look around at the only home she had known. If only I could see Ruth before I go, she thought.

The slow line of carts and animals moved through the rubble that was once their city. As they reached the edge of town, another caravan was seen.

"Stop, Father, please," cried Sarah. "I see Ruth." She jumped down and began to run. Ruth spoke as Sarah reached her. Quick tears clouded Sarah's eyes, "I can't understand you."

Ruth looked confused, then thoughtful. She repeated one word and held out her hands.

"Friends?" Sarah questioned. "Do you mean friends?"

Ruth nodded and a beautiful smile lightened her face.

"That is what you mean, isn't it?" cried Sarah.

The two girls hugged each other tightly, then Sarah's father called her to go. Sarah was sad to leave Ruth, but she was also happy inside. She thought, "I knew I would be able to understand Ruth. We knew what we were saying because we love each other. I wonder if love is the key to all understanding."

Sarah waved to Ruth until she could no longer see her. Then she turned to look forward; forward to a new future for her people who loved and served the true God.

THE BAPTISM

by Marion Schoeberlein

Matthias loved playing at the Jordan River. There were so many interesting things to see there; so many interesting people to watch. One of these was the man called John the Baptist.

He was a man with all the magic of freedom about him. Matthias studied his camel's hair coat and his leather girdle. He had never seen a man dressed like that.

"Repent ye, the kingdom of heaven is at hand!" John the Baptist shouted over and over to the listening crowd.

Matthias wondered what he meant. He didn't think he had too much to repent of. Sometimes he disobeyed his mother and father, sometimes he was jealous of his brother Simon, and once in a while he stole a fig from a vineyard, but all his friends did that.

They say he eats locusts and wild honey, Matthias thought, I'm glad I have better things to eat than that!

His parents laughed at him when he told them about John the Baptist.

"This man is very strange, my son," his father said, "it would be better for you to listen to the Scribes and Pharisees. They know our laws."

"He will surely come to trouble," his mother advised, shaking her head.

"But the people follow him," Matthias argued, "more and more of them come each day to be baptized by him!"

One day the crowd was larger than it had ever been. Matthias sat by the river, seeming to know that something special was going to happen.

He heard someone say, "Jesus, from Galilee, is going to be baptized today."

Matthias watched as Jesus came forward.

John the Baptist's loud voice thundered: "It is You who should baptize me. Why have You come to me?"

"Let it be so now," Jesus answered.

He stepped into the water, while the great throng watched.

John the Baptist held up his hands to baptize Jesus.

Matthias felt as if he, too, wanted to go into the water and be baptized.

His heart pounded.

Then he looked up and saw the sky open.

A beautiful dove descended from it and lighted on the head of Jesus.

"This is my beloved Son, in whom I am well pleased," a voice from the sky thundered.

The crowd stood gazing up into the sky.

This was the strangest baptism they had ever seen.

Surely this was no ordinary man. Could He be the one they had been promised?

Jesus' face shone with an incandescent light.

John the Baptist embraced him.

Matthias knew he would never witness a baptism like this again.

The Jordan seemed to glow with fire.

The words echoed in his ears again: "This is my beloved Son, in whom I am well pleased."

What did the words mean?

Someday soon I will find out, Matthias thought, and someday soon I will be baptized, too!

He went home feeling very happy with a miracle in his heart.

THE COLORFUL COVENANT

by Virginia L. Kroll

At first . . .

God grimaced.
Men muttered.
Women worried.

Noah knew.
He heeded,
Building bravely.
His family finished
The gathering great.

Soon . . .

Rain rippled.

Turtles tucked in.
Tapirs trembled.
Gulls gulped.
Finches flinched.
Penguins paced.
Pelicans panicked.
Aardvarks ambled.
Rhinos rambled.
Cranes cringed.
Cobras coiled.
Flamingos fluttered.
Caterpillars curled.
Sheep shivered.
Cattle cowered.
Porcupines prickled.
Badgers bristled.

Shortly . . .

Vegetation vanished.
Dirt disappeared.
Rivers roared.
The family floated.

Hyenas hunched.
Hedgehogs huddled.
Bearcats bellowed.
Groundhogs groaned.
Hippos huffed.
Sloths stirrred.
Otters uttered.
Seals sputtered.
Chipmunks chittered.
Titmice twittered.
Bees bumbled.
Magpies mumbled.
Warblers wept.
Deer despaired.

Then . . .

Winds whooshed.
Water waned.

Quails quieted.
Horses hushed.
Marmots mellowed.
Cougars calmed.
Llamas listened.
Hares hearkened.
Herrings heard.

The vessel veered,
Moored on a mount.
Dove departed.
Noah nestled,
Wearily waiting.
Dove disappointed.
One week went.

Finally . . .

God grinned.
Dove delivered
The broken branch.

Sun shone!

Loons laughed!
Leopards leaped!
Elands elated!
Jackals jumped!
Donkeys delighted!
Rabbits rejoiced!
Peacocks pranced!
Ducks danced!
Rheas reeled!
Skuas squealed!
Weavers wove!
Spiders spun!
Cheetahs cheered!
Storks strutted!
Fireflies flitted!
Glowworms glittered!
Snails swirled!
Tumblebugs twirled!

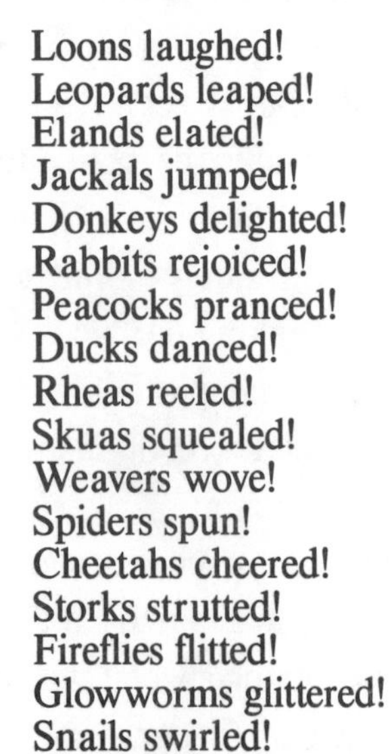

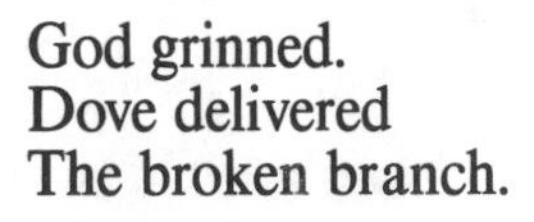

At last . . .

The family frolicked.
Noah nodded.
Rainbow reflected.
"Amen!" he added.

EMOE AND THE KING

by Jennifer Watts

Emoe Rabbit's gray ears twitched as he awoke with a start. He thought he had heard someone crying. It wasn't Mama or Papa Rabbit. They were still asleep in their corner of the burrow. Then he heard it again. The sound came from outside the rock pile where Emoe lived.

Emoe crept to the nearest peephole in the rocks around his burrow. He could not believe what he saw! A strange procession was winding its way up the hill into the garden. Right away, Emoe recognized the man who led the train of people. He and two other men had just finished carving a big hole in the hillside near Emoe's rock pile. The men had called him "Master Joseph."

What is that white thing Master Joseph is helping to carry? wondered Emoe. And why are those women crying?

Emoe wanted to get a better look, so he scampered outside and hid behind a small lilac bush. Emoe watched as the men carried the white thing into the big hole in the hillside. It looked like a human body wrapped from head to toe in white cloth! Whatever the thing was, Master Joseph and the other men left it inside. Then they covered the hole up with a huge stone.

Soon everyone left except two women. They stood near the big stone, still weeping.

Why are they so sad? wondered Emoe.

Then one of the women spoke. "Mary, we must go. The Sabbath will soon begin."

"How could they do this to our King?" sobbed Mary. "I heard a Roman soldier talking about how they beat him. Then they made a crown of thorns and placed it on his head."

"I don't know how they could do this thing, Mary," said the other woman. "Our Lord did no wrong. He loved his enemies. Even as he died on the cross, he asked God to forgive them. But thanks to that good man, Joseph, he now has a peaceful tomb to rest in."

Emoe watched the two sad women leave. So the big hole is a tomb, he thought. And a king is buried in the tomb!

Emoe dashed back to his burrow under the rock pile. Mama and Papa were awake now.

"Mama! Papa! cried Emoe. "A king is buried in the tomb outside!"

"Oh, Emoe," said Mama, "your imagination is getting out of hand."

"Come with us, Emoe," said Papa. "We're going to the clover patch."

Emoe could tell Papa was annoyed so he went obediently with them. Soon he had eaten all the clover he could hold. Suddenly, Emoe's long ears moved to catch a strange sound. Then he saw them! Roman soldiers were all over the garden! One soldier went to the tomb. He stretched a seal across the large stone.

Emoe could hear two soldiers talking. "Why should we guard the tomb? A dead man cannot harm anyone," said one soldier.

"This man claimed to be the Son of God," replied the other soldier. "He also said he would rise again after three days and nights. We must make sure his friends don't steal him from the tomb and say that he is risen."

Emoe carefully made his way back to the burrow. Mama and Papa were already there. Mama was furious!

"We'll just have to pack up and move," said Mama. "This noise is driving me crazy."

"But Mama," said Emoe, "I heard the soldiers say they'd be here only three days and nights."

Mama calmed down. "Well, I hate to leave this lovely garden. Maybe I can stand it that long."

Those were the longest three days and nights Emoe had ever known. He kept thinking about what the soldiers said. What if the king did rise from the dead? He shivered at the thought.

It was near dawn after the third night. Mama and Papa were sleeping soundly, but Emoe was too excited to sleep. Through his peephole, he watched the soldiers. Suddenly, a bolt of lightning streaked across the sky. Then the earth began to tremble! Emoe heard the soldiers scream in terror.

Then Emoe saw a strange form at the entrance of the tomb. It was all shiny and white.

"It's an angel!" cried the guards. They fainted because they were so afraid.

Emoe watched in amazement as the angel broke the seal and rolled the great stone away! When the soldiers awoke and saw what was happening, they ran away, screaming and yelling.

Before long someone else entered the garden. Emoe recognized the two women who had cried at the tomb. The women looked very frightened when they saw the angel. Then the angel spoke. "Fear not. The one whom ye seek is not here. He is risen. Come, see where he lay."

Emoe could stand it no longer. He had to see for himself. In seconds he was darting into the tomb behind the women. Sure enough, the tomb was empty! Only a heap of white rags lay in the corner.

"Go and tell his friends that he is risen," the angel told the women.

As the women left, Emoe shuddered. A frightening thought crossed his mind. It had to be a ghost! How else could he have left the tomb? The entrance was sealed, until the angel broke the seal.

Terrified, Emoe ran from the tomb. Then he stopped dead in his tracks! Through the early morning mist, Emoe could see the two women on the trail just ahead of him. They were talking to a man dressed all in white, like the angel.

Emoe crept behind the big stone which the angel had rolled away from the tomb entrance. He could hear the woman talking.

"Truly, it is Jesus, our Master," said the woman named Mary.

The women then knelt at the man's feet and worshipped him as if he were a king.

A king! thought Emoe. This must be the king who was buried in the tomb. But the king was dead, and this man didn't look at all like a ghost. He was a real, live man.

Then Emoe heard the man speak. It was the most gentle voice he had ever heard. "Be not afraid. Go tell my brethren they shall see me in Galilee," said this man whom Mary had called Jesus.

Emoe watched the women run joyfully to tell the news. When he glanced back around, the white figure was gone. But Emoe was no longer afraid. A warm, gentle feeling flowed through his body. He knew that this King, named Jesus, had indeed risen from the dead and was now very much alive.

Emoe returned to the burrow where Mama and Papa were still sleeping. I wonder if they will believe me when I tell them that the King has risen, thought Emoe, as he drifted off into dreamland too.

BIBLE PLAYS

. . . AND SONGS

PLAYS AND MUSICALS

School or church plays are the perfect opportunity to give youngsters the experience they need to develop their whole selves. Drama offers a range of learning, which develops individual abilities in vocal skills and good articulation. On stage, children are given the chance to enrich worship while rejoicing.

A few tips may be helpful for preparing your children for the big performance:

1. Begin by reading the play to the children.
2. Be very sure they understand the meaning of all words and have some idea of the background of the characters.
3. Re-read the play, asking various children to repeat the lines (if they cannot read). For readers, have them read various parts as you continue through the play.
4. Listen for their interpretation of certain characters before selecting the cast.
5. When parts have been selected, then children must memorize before rehearsal. Do not tire the children with long rehearsal periods. Shorter rehearsals over a longer period of time aid in producing better results. We want dramatization to be a joy not a task!

Many of the plays that follow have a song or two that can be weaved into the play to create a musical. Be creative. You or your students may want to create new verses for the songs to include in your musical. Other popular Christian hymns may also be included in your performance. If you plan to use the songs to create a musical, here are some suggestions:

1. Sing the song(s) with the children. Practice singing only for initial rehearsals. The entire cast should learn all the verses to be performed.
2. Assign solo parts where you feel your cast members have the ability and where it is appropriate.
3. If accompaniment is not available at each rehearsal, practice with taped music.
4. Decide where the song will be used during the play and practice singing while rehearsing the playscript.
5. Experiment by playing the song(s) softly in the background during narration, or set the proper mood as audience is entering and leaving auditorium. ENJOY CASTING!

THREE MEN IN THE FIERY FURNACE

by Colleen Westberg

Cast: (all citizens of Babylon)

Tamar	Rhoda
Ira	Issachar (paper boy)

Issachar: Get your Babylon Bulletin here! Read a Babylon Bulletin, only two shekels!

Tamar: Have you read today's Babylon Bulletin yet?

Ira: No, I haven't had a chance. Why?

Tamar: You'll never guess what that King Nebuchadnezzar is up to now!

Ira: It's hard to tell! He had a crazy dream a while back. He couldn't even tell the wise men what it was about, but he still expected them to interpret it! Naturally no one in all of Babylon was successful. Finally one of the Israelite slaves told its meaning. Daniel, I think his name was. Now Daniel's been made a big shot in the Babylonian government.

Tamar: Well, this is even wilder than a nightmare! Old Nebuchadnezzar is going to put up a statue ninety feet high and nine feet wide, made out of gold!

Ira: Imagine what that will do to our taxes!

Rhoda: That's not all. At the dedication ceremony, all the rulers of the government from the whole country have to come and bow down to this idol.

Ira: What an egomaniac, that Nebuchadnezzar has gone too far!

Tamar: If anyone refuses to bow down, they will be thrown into a furnace of blazing fire!

Ira: Oh, come off it, Tamar. Are you reading the Babylon Bulletin or the Provincial Enquirer?

Tamar: I'm being perfectly serious, Ira!

Rhoda I wonder what those Israelite nobles will do? I've heard they worship only their God, Yahweh. Surely they won't want to bow down to Nebuchadnezzar's golden arch! But then again, what choice do they have?

(*All leave.*)

Issachar: Extra! Extra! Special edition! Read all about it! Three Israelites refuse to bow down to Nebuchadnezzar's idol. King orders them burned! Everyone invited to the fireworks!

(*Issachar leaves.*)

Rhoda: See, what did I tell you? Nothing can save those Israelites now! They don't have a prayer . . . or do they?

(*Rhoda leaves.*)

Issachar: Extra! Extra! News flash! Read all about it! Shadrach, Meshach, and Abed-nego survive the fiery furnace! Say their faith in God has saved them! Nebuchadnezzar acknowledges the God of Israel!

Ira: Well, some mighty amazing things are happening during our time, ladies.

Rhoda: I think we ought to find out more about this God of the Israelites!

Use the song, "Shadrach, Meshach, Abed-Nego" found on page 40, to turn this play into a lively musical.

DANIEL'S THREE FRIENDS

Words and Music by Helen Friesen

SHADRACH, MESHACH, ABED-NEGO

Words and Music by Diane Beck

VERSE 2

The flames were so hot that the men who threw them in
Were killed by the heat of the fiery din.
When Nebuchadnezzar looked in the fire once more,
Behold, there were not three men, there were four.

VERSE 3

The king called unto them to come from the flames
Not a hair on their heads or their bodies had changed.
The king was astonished and changed his decree.
Now, no one would speak against the God of these three!

NOAH AND THE ARK

By Edith E. Cutting

Cast: Noah
Shem
Ham
Japheth
Narrator
Noah's Wife
Shem's Wife
Ham's Wife
Japheth's Wife

Narrator: In the days when the world was new, God found that the people He had created were doing evil things. He was disappointed and angry with all of them except Noah, who was a good man. Therefore, He told Noah how to build a great ark, or boat. Inside the ark, Noah and his family would be safe when God made a great flood to destroy all those that had not obeyed Him. (Genesis 6:5-18)

Scene I

(*Noah and his sons are in front of the ark.*)

Noah: We have the ark almost done now, my sons. It is three hundred cubits long, just as the Lord commanded.

Shem: And fifty cubits wide, and thirty cubits high. We measured it with our own arms, elbows to fingertips.

Ham: The hard gopher wood it is made of is strong, too. No wonder God told you to use that.

Japheth: Did He tell you when it must be finished? We still have to make the door to close that opening in the side.

Noah: No, He did not say what day the flood might begin. We do not know His times.

Shem: This certainly is the biggest thing we have ever built. I wonder why He said to make it three stories high?

Ham: We have spent so much time building it. Would we have done better just to climb high up in the mountains?

Japheth: What if the pitch hasn't sealed all the cracks? Will it really float when the floods come?

Noah: My sons, do not doubt the Lord our God. He commanded me, and He commands the waters as well. We shall be safe.

Narrator: So with Noah's faith and obedience, the ark was finished. There was room for Noah and his wife, and his sons with their wives. The next thing God required of Noah was to save two of all living things. He must also provide food enough for all of them. (Genesis 6:18-22)

Scene II

(*Noah, his sons, and some animals are in front of the ark.*)

Noah:	Shem! Ham! Help me drive in these animals and the birds.
Shem:	Do we have to bring the creeping things, too?
Noah:	Yes, everything. And Japheth, bring grain and grass and whatever else is needed to feed them.
Japheth:	Yes, Father, I have been gathering it.
Ham:	Bring food for us, too!
Japheth:	Don't worry. Our wives are taking care of that.
Ham:	Is it all right to take three or four of a kind if they want to come?
Noah:	No, God said only two, a male and a female of each living creature.
Shem:	Does that mean God is going to save the life of all kinds of things in spite of the flood?
Noah:	He is always merciful. Somehow He will give us all a new start.
Japheth:	Some of those creatures don't want to get on the ark.
Noah:	No matter. Drive them or lead them, but make sure we do not miss any living thing, for so the Lord God commanded.
Narrator:	As soon as Noah and his sons got all the living creatures into the ark, they and their wives went in and the Lord shut the great door. Then the rains began. (Genesis 7: 13-21)

Scene III

(*Noah and his wife are in the ark, looking out.*)

Wife: Oh, my husband, look at the rain! It is pouring down like rivers.

Noah: And look at the rivers. They are overflowing their banks. The water is spreading over the fields like lakes.

Wife: Noah, did you feel that? The ark is floating!

Noah: Yes, the waters have lifted it up. But we are safe and dry.

Wife: Oh, Noah, you were so wise to build this ark as God commanded.

Noah: Only God is wise. We must thank Him for having warned us and teaching us what to do.

Wife: See, the water is rising so fast even the mountains will soon be covered.

Noah: Yes. Look there. The tip of the last one has disappeared. The rain and the flood are all we can see now.

Wife: Just water. Rain coming down above us, deep waters underneath, and waves on the sea all around.

Noah: What power God has, so to control the earth and the sea, and all that is in them!

Wife: Noah, will we ever see the earth again?

Noah: Have faith, my wife. God had us save all these creatures. Surely He will bring man and beast, flying fowl and creeping things back to Earth.

Narrator: It was a long and wearisome time. Everyone and everything alive was shut up in the ark. There was little space to move around, and Noah's family got tired of seeing the same things all the time. (Genesis 8:1-4)

Scene IV

(*Shem and his wife are looking out from the ark.*)

Wife: Oh, Shem, my husband, when will the water ever go away?

Shem: In God's good time. We must be patient.

Wife: I am tired of being patient. I have kept count, and we have already been in the ark 150 days.

Shem: I know. It may be so for a long time yet.

Wife: And I'm tired of eating the same old dry food all the time.

Shem: I thought I felt a bump.

Wife: Do you suppose we have touched land?

Shem: Oh, no. We are above even the mountains, and all this water cannot drain away at once.

Wife: I can't wait to walk on the ground again, and be steady. Here we are always swaying with the waves. Sometimes it makes me feel sick.

Shem: Well, we have stopped moving now. Let's go ask my father, Noah, if he knows where we are. Perhaps we have touched the tip of a mountain.

Wife: If it's any kind of land, I shall be glad.

Shem: Yes, praise God that the earth is still there. Soon we may walk again in His solid world.

Narrator: The ark had indeed touched land, but only the very top of Mount Ararat. Two months passed before the waters went down far enough so that Noah could see even the tips of the other mountains. More days passed. At last he opened the window and let a raven fly out, and then a dove, to see what they could find. (Genesis 8:5-9)

Scene V

(*Ham and his wife look out from the ark.*)

Ham: The raven has not come back. He must have found a perching place.

Wife: It may be that he fell into the water and can never come back. I am afraid, Ham. Suppose we fall into the water when we try to leave.

Ham: We are safe here, and the water is going down. Besides, the dove came safely back.

Wife: I know, but . . .

Ham: Perhaps the raven has stronger wings and has flown farther.

Wife: How I wish I had wings to fly. Sometimes I'm afraid we may be shut in here forever.

Ham: Do not say that, my wife. We waited forty days before my father let the birds fly out, but they were free to go at last. So shall we.

Wife: Yes, I suppose we can wait seven more days till he sends the dove again, but I fear . . .

Ham: Do not fear. Truly, we must wait in faith.

Narrator: After seven days Noah did send the dove out again. Everybody watched anxiously all day. (Genesis 8:10-14)

SS1870

Scene VI

(*Japheth and his wife are looking out from the ark.*)

Wife: Japheth, my husband, isn't it exciting? It has been so long since we walked the earth.

Japheth: I have talked with my father. When the dove brings a token, we will stay inside only a few more days for the earth to dry.

Wife: But can't we open the door a little and step out? The ark must be stranded on land. Even if I stepped in water, I would be happy to feel the ground underneath.

Japheth: No, no, my wife. Be patient. Think of all the animals that would crowd to the door if we opened it a bit.

Wife: I suppose so. They must be as eager as I am. I can hardly wait.

Japheth: Look! Look! The dove is back, and there is something in its beak!

Wife: An olive leaf! Oh, there are trees again! Do you remember the olive trees where we lived before?

Japheth: And the figs, and the almond trees!

Wife: And the vineyards. How beautiful they were!

Japheth: Surely God is making the earth ready once again.

Wife: And we shall see it bear fruit as it did before!

Narrator: At last their faith and patience were rewarded, and God spoke to Noah. The time had come for them to leave the ark. Noah and his sons opened the big door. All the animals, birds, and creeping things came crowding forth, and after them, the people. (Genesis 8:15-19)

Scene VII

(*All the living beings are standing in front of the ark.*)

Noah: How wonderful the fresh air feels!

Noah's wife: And the sunshine! I had almost forgotten what it looked like.

Shem: It is good to have room to stretch.

Shem's wife: Yes, it is good not to be crowded, and to walk on firm ground.

Ham: And to see the earth itself again! Even the dirt feels good to my fingers.

Ham's wife: Oh, Ham, my eyes were wearied with looking only at water.

Japheth: It won't be long until vines and grains start growing. We shall have fresh fruit, and the animals will find more food.

Japheth's wife: I know. You were worried for fear we had not brought enough.

Noah:	Surely the Lord knew what was needed. He measured the ark to provide for all.
Shem:	Maybe He enclosed us in the ark to make us realize how big His Earth really is.
Ham:	And how safe we are in His hands, on water or on the earth.
Japheth:	I hardly know what to do now that we don't have to watch over the other creatures every minute.
Noah:	What to do? I know. We shall build an altar to our God!
Narrator:	Noah and his sons built the altar, ready to offer sacrifice, and God made a covenant with them. God promised that never again would He send such a terrible flood. As a sign of His promise, He put the rainbow in the sky. It would appear when there was rain; as a reminder that water would not flood the whole earth ever again. (Genesis 8:20-22 and 9:8-13)

Scene VIII

(*All the people are standing before the altar and looking up at the rainbow.*)

Noah:	See how God's bow of many colors arches across the sky.
Noah's wife:	It's colors remind me of all the flowers on His Earth.
Shem's wife:	Even the green of the leaves is there.
Shem:	And the bow joins clouds and sunshine.
Ham:	It is curved like the very arm of God enfolding the earth.
Ham's wife:	As if we were His children.
Japheth's wife:	As if the whole world were in His care.
Japheth:	It is. We know the whole earth is in His care.
Noah's wife:	What peace to know it will nevermore be flooded to destruction!
Noah:	Yes, we can always feel safe, for the rainbow seals God's covenant forever.

FAITHFUL OLD NOAH

Words by Phyllis Whitaker
Music by Helen Friesen

F Bb/F F Gm C F/A F Bb C
6. No - ah and his fam-'ly did as they were told, Told in the Bi-ble in the days of old, They
(7. The) Lord said, "No-ah, now go in - side, Make your-self com-fort-able for this long ride."
(8. Ben) Gon-na woke up with a start that night. What was that sound on the roof out - side? A
(9. The) wat-ter rose swift-ly the ark float - ed a - way, The Lord kept His prom - ise to No - ah that day.
6. 7. 8.
A Dm Gm Dm/A Gm/Bb C7/Bb F/A F C F Fm G6 G C
gath - ered the an - i - mals two by two just as the Lord had told them to.
No - ah went in; The Lord closed the door and out-side the ark it be - gan to pour.
sin - gle tear fell from Ben Gon - na's eye and then he knew that No - ah was right.
F Gm C A Dm Gm C
"Faith-ful old No - ah, you faith-ful old man; You're build - ing the ark on the bone - dry land.
Sil - ly old No - ah, you sil - ly old man, You built your boat on the bone - dry land.
Sil - ly old No - ah, you sil - ly old man, You built your boat on the bone - dry land.
D.S.
Faith-ful old No - ah, you faith-ful old man, You build your boat just as I com - mand." 7. The
Sil - ly old No - ah, you sil - ly old man, You built your boat where no rain was planned." 8. Ben
Sil - ly old No - ah, you sil - ly old man, You built your boat at the Lord's com - mand." 9. The
9.
A Dm Gm F/A C Am Am/C Dm Dm7 Gm C C7 F
Faith - ful old No - ah, you faith - ful old man, you built your boat on the bone - dry land.

NOAH AND THE ANIMALS

Words and Music by Helen Friesen

There went spotted leopards, two hippopotami,
Owls and hawks and eagles, they came on the fly.
All the cooing pigeons flew up to their perch,
While the mother rabbit for a home did search.

See the colored feathers on the parrot's wing,
Robins, larks and sparrows, all of them could sing.
Noah had no need to save a space for fish,
They could swim in water everywhere they wish.

Tigers came with stripes and also zebras, too,
Hear the donkeys braying, we can do that, too.
Elephants came plodding, see them swing their trunks,
Give the angry rhino room to find a bunk.

Even wolves and foxes hurried to get on,
Then they tried to sleep until another dawn.
Snapping alligators, with their bumpy hide,
With their swishing tails, they pushed it all aside.

Watch the king of beasts, the lion on the prowl,
You can hear the coyotes putting up a howl.
Swift of foot are cheetahs, also many deer,
Ducks and geese together, them you never fear.

Can you count the humps upon the camel's back?
Don't you dare to tangle with the moose's rack,
When the sow lay down you heard a heavy thud,
She was disappointed, for there was no mud.

Who will pet the kittens? They're so soft and nice,
You can hear them purr, but who let in the mice?
Listen to the noise the angry badger makes,
If he keeps on snarling, he'll keep all awake.

Don't provoke the skunk for no one wants to smell
What would really happen, but that we all know well,
Snakes in diff'rent sizes, bring up the rear,
They were left alone by Noah, never fear.

THE LORD IS GOD!

by Marilyn Senterfitt

One of the most dramatic moments in the Old Testament is the contest on Mount Carmel between Elijah and the prophets of Baal. The following is based on I Kings 18 (RSV).

CAST: Speaking parts—Elijah, Obadiah, Ahab, Widow, two Israelites, two Baal prophets, the chorus. Remainder of cast includes Israelites and prophets.

SCENERY AND PROPS: Twenty or more shoeboxes or similar cardboard boxes sealed and painted gray or brown, pieces of wood, large yellow circle of poster board to represent sun, a large, bright red cloth, four water jugs and dried up greenery, either real or made from poster board, two bulls made of poster board and cut in large pieces, several pots and pans.

COSTUMES: Chorus wears white tops and dark skirts or pants, Baal prophets dress in black or brown robes, Israelites wear many-colored robes, Elijah's clothes should be rough resembling an animal skin, Obadiah should be in a brightly colored robe, and Ahab should be in a gold-trimmed robe wearing a crown of yellow poster board. Robes may be made following instructions found on page 87-90.

SET THE SCENE: Using eight to ten cardboard "stones" set up Baal altar on stage left. Scatter twelve "stones" around on stage right. Dried up greenery may be placed at various points. Position cut up bulls near Baal altar and the scattered stones. Place pile of wood nearby. Water jugs are offstage. Place red cloth on floor in front of chorus. Yellow sun is placed to left of chorus and pots and pans are placed at feet of assigned chorus members.

(*Chorus enters both stage left and right and stands in middle in the background. Ahab enters stage right and stands near front of stage. Obadiah hurries in from stage left and bows before Ahab. He rises.*)

Obadiah: O mighty Ahab, I have come with news about Elijah.

Ahab: Tell me he is dead and make me a happy man!

Obadiah: No, I have just now spoken to him.

Ahab: What! Where is that evil man who brought this terrible drought upon my kingdom?

Obadiah: He comes now, your highness.

(*Eiljah enters stage left. Ahab moves to meet him.*)

Ahab: So it's you, is it? The man who brought disaster upon Israel!

Elijah: You are talking about yourself! It was you and your evil queen who refused to obey God and instead worship stone idols.

Ahab: Queen Jezebel has the right to worship whom she pleases. If the people wish to follow, that is no fault of ours.

Elijah: This matter must be settled. I challenge the prophets of Baal to a contest. Send all 450 of them to Mount Carmel and the prophets of Asherah also. The people of Israel must witness this contest. Send forth messengers and call them all to Mount Carmel. They will see with their own eyes who is the one true and powerful God.

(*Ahab turns to Obadiah.*)
Ahab: Obadiah, do all that he says. This fool must be put in his place once and for all.

(*Obadiah exits stage left. Ahab follows and also exits stage left as Elijah exits stage right.*)

Chorus: (Boys) Elijah has challenged the prophets of Baal to a contest.
(Girls) Poor Elijah! He will be only one against so many.
(Boys and Girls) Look! The prophets are coming!

(*Prophets enter stage left and gather around the Baal altar.*)

Chorus: (Girls) The people of Israel have been called to see the contest.
(Boys) Poor Elijah! They will surely laugh at him.
(Girls and Boys) Now the people are coming!

(*Israelites enter from stage right and stand around. Widow and two Israelites move to center stage.*)

First Israelite: This will be a quick contest. Elijah doesn't have a chance against Baal.

Second Israelite: You're right! That man must be crazy. He even claimed His God brought this drought upon us.

Widow: You're both so wrong about Elijah.

(*Israelites turn and glare at Widow.*)

First Israelite: You aren't from around here. What do you know of this matter?

Widow: Three years ago Elijah came to my village and asked for food and water. I had none to spare, but his God brought a miracle and provided food for us. Then my son became ill and died. I blamed Elijah but he took my dead son in his arms and carried him to his room. In a short while my son walked out of that room alive! Elijah's God had brought him back to life!

Second Israelite: I don't believe a word of this! Come, Isaac, let's be sure to find a good spot to watch this Elijah make a fool of himself.

(*Israelites move away laughing. Widow moves to stage right as Obadiah enters stage left.*)

Obadiah: Bow down all ye people. The King is coming! The King is coming!

(*Ahab enters stage left and stands near Obadiah and the Baal prophets. The Israelites and Baal prophets bow down.*)

Chorus: The contest will soon begin, for Elijah is coming!

(*Israelites and prophets rise as Elijah enters stage right and stands near scattered stones. Israelites and prophets whisper among themselves and some point at Elijah and laugh.*)

Elijah: You people are trying to worship many gods. You must decide who is truly Lord. If it is God, then follow Him. If it is Baal, then follow him.

Chorus: (*Sings "How Long Will You Waver?" Verse may be repeated.*)

Elijah: I am the only prophet of God that is left, (*points to Baal prophets*) but Baal has 450. The time has come to see who worships the true God. Here are two young bulls prepared for sacrifice. You prophets lay wood and the bull on your altar. Then pray to Baal to set that wood afire and consume the sacrifice. I will do the same.

Chorus: (Boys) That is a fair contest.
(Girls) But who will win?
(Boys and Girls) Let the contest begin!

Elijah: The prophets of Baal can be first since there are so many of them and only one of me. Let's see if Baal can set the wood afire.

First Baal Prophet: This is an easy task for our mighty god. Elijah, you will never have a chance to even set up your altar.

(*Prophets place wood and cut up bull on altar. They move around the altar waving arms and praying in loud voices for Baal to send the fire. Elijah lays on stage with head propped on elbow.*)

Elijah: You'll have to shout louder than that to get your god's attention. Perhaps he is on a trip, or asleep or talking to someone else. You're just going to have to shout louder.

Chorus: (*Sings "Shout Louder!"*)

(*Elijah stands and chorus passes yellow sun from left to right over their heads.*)

Elijah: You have shouted and prayed all day long. Baal has not sent a spark or flicker to light the fire. Now it is my turn. All of you gather closer to me.

(*Israelites move closer to Elijah. He begins to stack the twelve "stones" making an altar.*)

Elijah: These twelve stones represent the twelve tribes of Israel.

(*He places wood and cut up animal on the altar. Taking a piece of wood Elijah pretends to dig a trench around the altar.*)

Elijah: You men bring four jugs of water and pour over the altar.

(*Four Israelites move offstage and return with the water jugs. They pretend to pour water over altar.*)

Elijah: Do it again.

(*Repeat the action.*)

Elijah: Now do it again.

(*Action is repeated. Israelites and prophets are whispering and becoming restive. Many are mocking Elijah.*)

Second Baal Prophet: No god is that powerful. The wood is soaked. It cannot be set afire.

Ahab: I told you that Elijah is a fool.

Obadiah: I am not so sure, your highness.

Ahab: Who asked your opinion?

(*After final jug is emptied Elijah bows down before the altar and raises arms above his head and looks to the sky.*)

Elijah: O Lord God of Abraham, Isaac and Israel, prove today that you are the God of Israel and I am your servant; prove that I have done all this at your command. O Lord, answer me! Answer me so these people will know that you are God and that you have brought them back to yourself.

(*Everyone looks up to sky. Assigned chorus members bang pots and pans together. Lights may be turned on and off. Assigned chorus members pick up red cloth and quickly throw over the altar and return to chorus.*)

First Israelite: It isn't possible! The whole altar is on fire. Everything is burning!

Widow: I tried to tell you Elijah's God is the most powerful.

Second Israelite: I would not have believed it if I had not seen it with my own eyes.

(*Israelites one by one bow down. Baal prophets cover their eyes and exit stage left. Obadiah moves to the altar and bows. Ahab looks around and realizes he is alone. He rushes to exit stage left.*)

Chorus: (*Sings "The Lord Is God!"*)

(*Israelites and Elijah stand and join chorus in repeating "The Lord Is God!"*)

HOW LONG WILL YOU WAVER?

Text based on I Kings 18:21 — Words and Music by Helen Friesen

SHOUT LOUDER!

Text based on I Kings 18:27 Words and Music by Helen Friesen

THE LORD IS GOD!

Text based on I Kings 18:39 Words and Music by Helen Friesen

THE GOOD SAMARITAN

by Helen Kitchell Evans

Cast: Samaritan
Traveler
Innkeeper
Narrator

Narrator: Scene I takes place on the road to Jericho. A traveler has been robbed by thieves. He has been beaten. So far two people have noticed him and walked by. Now enters another. Let us watch as he enters. (*The beaten man lies on floor.*)

Samaritan: (*Enters, walks by the beaten man, then returns to him.*) What has happened to you?

Traveler: I have been robbed by thieves. They beat me and took some of my clothes.

Samaritan: You are wounded. Here, let me tie my handkerchief around your arm. That will help you.

Traveler: People have passed by, but did not stop to help me. You are very kind to stop.

Samaritan: Come, try to get up. I'll take you to an inn for the night.

Traveler: (*Gets up slowly with help.*) You are very, very kind.

Narrator: The Samaritan has now walked with the traveler to an inn. As scene II opens he is about to knock on the door of an inn.

Samaritan: (*Knocks.*) (*Innkeeper appears.*) Could we get a room for the night?

Innkeeper: Who is this wounded man?

Samaritan: A man I found along the road. He has been beaten and robbed of money and clothes.

Innkeeper: Come in. (*They step forward to show entrance to inn.*)

Samaritan: In the morning I must leave. Take care of this man. (*Hands money to innkeeper.*) And whatever else it costs I'll pay in full when I come again.

Innkeeper: Very well. I will keep him here until he is able to go on his way. You have been very kind to this stranger. Not many people would be so kind. You are a good Christian man.

Traveler: God bless you for what you have done for me. I'll never forget your kindness.

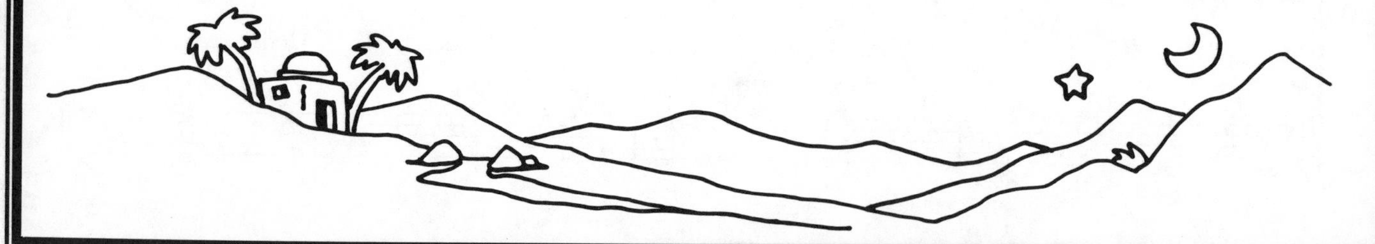

DANIEL INTERPRETS A DREAM

by Helen Kitchell Evans

Scene I

Court of King Nebuchadnezzar

Cast:	
King Nebuchadnezzar	Magicians
Daniel	Four Chaldeans
Enchanters	Servants
Sorcerers	Narrator

Narrator: In the second year of the reign of King Nebuchadnezzar, he had dreams and his spirit was troubled. He could not sleep. When the scene opens we see him ringing for his servants.

(*As the King rings for servants any number may enter.*)

First Servant: You rang, your majesty?

King Nebuchadnezzar: Yes, call the magicians, the enchanters, the sorcerers and the Chaldeans. I wish to tell them my dreams. (*Two servants leave the stage and bring in these people.*) (*Any number.*)
I have dreamed a dream. My spirit is troubled.

Chaldean: O King! Live forever. Tell us the dream and we will show you the meaning.

King Nebuchadnezzar: The dream has left me. Tell me what I dreamed or you shall suffer! Show me the dream and the meaning and you shall be rewarded and have great honor.

Second Chaldean: Let the King tell his dreams to his servants and we will tell him the meaning.

Third Chaldean: There is not a man upon the earth than can show the King's dream to him.

Fourth Chaldean: No Lord or ruler ever asked such a thing of a Chaldean.

All Magicians: Or of the magicians.

Enchanters and Sorcerers: Nor any of us.

King Nebuchadnezzar: I will destroy the wise men of Babylon!

Curtain

Scene II

Daniel before King

Narrator: So the decree went forth that the wise men were to be slain. They sought Daniel and his companions to be slain, also. They had been telling people the meaning of their dreams. Then Daniel asked the captain of the King's guard for an appointment with the King. During the night God had revealed the dream to Daniel and he asked that the wise men not be killed. Scene II opens now with Daniel before the King. Servants are present.

King Nebuchadnezzar: They tell me that you can interpret my dream.

Daniel: The secret that you have demanded cannot be told by wise men, enchanters, magicians, nor soothsayers. But there is a God in heaven that reveals secrets and he has told King Nebuchadnezzar what shall happen in the latter days.

King Nebuchadnezzar: Yes, yes, please go on!

Daniel: You saw a great image whose brightness was excellent. The head was of fine gold, and the arms and breast of silver, the body of brass and its legs were part iron and part clay. A great stone smote the image and it broke into pieces which the wind carried away. The stone that smote the image became a great mountain. It filled the whole earth.

King Nebuchadnezzar: Tell me more! This is the dream I had! Tell me more!

Daniel: You are a great king. After you, (*Pause.*) another kingdom, inferior to yours, shall rise. A third shall rule over the earth. A fourth shall crush the earth! It shall be divided like the iron and clay feet and legs. It shall be partly strong and partly broken. In those days shall God of heaven set up a kingdom which shall never be destroyed.

King Nebuchadnezzar: (*Falls on his face before Daniel.*)
Let us offer an oblation to Daniel. Your God is the God of Gods and the Lord of Lords, a revealer of secrets. You shall be great! Bring him many gifts and servants! He shall rule over Babylon!

BOAZ' KINDNESS TO RUTH

by Kay Erlandson

Cast and Costumes:

Ruth:	Long skirt, or apron, and a basket with handle
Naomi:	Similar outfit
Boaz:	Brightly colored shirt with wide cloth belt
Three workers:	Large shirts in neutral colors

Setting: This story takes place in Bethlehem at the beginning of grain harvest. Naomi and her daughter-in-law, Ruth, live alone since the death of both of their husbands.

Naomi: Ruth, we are almost out of food. It is time to find a way to get some barley so I can make flour for bread.

Ruth: Please, let me go to the fields and I will pick up the grain which the workers drop as they work.

Naomi: Go ahead and see what you can find. Whatever grain you pick will be helpful.

(*Ruth goes to the field and picks the barley which has fallen onto the ground. The owner of the field, Boaz, comes to see how the workers are doing.*)

Boaz (*To workers.*): Hello. How is the work going? God bless you as you work.

Worker 1: Hello, sir. We are picking a lot of grain today.

Boaz: Who is that woman out in the field?

Worker 2: She came to Bethlehem with Naomi. I think her name is Ruth.

Worker 3: She came early this morning and asked if she could pick the leftover grain. She has been working hard.

(*Boaz walks over to talk with Ruth.*)

Boaz: My workers tell me that your name is Ruth. You may pick as much grain as you wish. I have told my workers not to bother you and you may even pick right beside them. There is water in the jugs which you may drink when you get thirsty.

Ruth: Thank you, sir. But why are you being so kind to me when you don't even know me?

Boaz: Ruth, I have heard how nice you have been to Naomi. I know that you left your family and home to move here with Naomi. May God bless your work.

(*Boaz leaves Ruth and returns to his workers.*)

Boaz: You workers be sure to drop some extra grain for Ruth to pick.

(*Ruth returns to Naomi with her basket.*)

Ruth: Naomi, look at all this grain. We will be able to make a lot of flour.

Naomi: God has truly blessed us, Ruth. You will be able to gather grain from Boaz' field for a long time. We will have plenty of food. Boaz has been kind to us.

JOSEPH DREAM WEAVER

by Helen Kitchell Evans

Cast: Pharaoh
Butler
Joseph
First Servant
Second Servant
Two Magicians
Narrator

(*This play may be given in a church chancel. No curtain need be used. The players may come out while the narrator is reading and set the stage for the play. Artificial palms may be used. Pillows, a rug, a bell and some dishes of fruit will be needed. Items mentioned in the play include a ring and a gold chain. The aim of all dramatic activity is pleasure. Children gain much knowledge when they present such an activity before their church congregation. It is not necessary to have elaborate settings for simple plays.*)

Narrator: Jacob lived in the land of Canaan. He had twelve sons but of these he was most fond of Joseph. One day he made a coat of many colors. Joseph put on this coat and went to the place where his brothers were herding sheep. The brothers saw Joseph coming and were jealous of him.

Joseph had been dreaming and he told his brothers what the dreams meant. "Someday all of you will have to bow down to me."

The jealous brothers decided to kill Joseph. One brother, Reuben, said, "Let us not kill him. Let us shed no blood. Instead, let us throw him into a pit and leave him there." Reuben figured that he could get him out later and take him home.

The brothers agreed. They took off his coat and threw him in a pit. Then they sat down to eat. Soon a company of Ishmaelites came by. Judah, another brother, said, "Let's sell Joseph." So they did and when Joseph came to Egypt he was thrown in prison for something that he did not do. God knew Joseph had done no wrong and He was with him.

(*The scene opens with Pharaoh resting on pillows, a gong is to his right and he is surrounded with palms. He is awakened suddenly. He has been dreaming and is much troubled. He rings for servants. They enter hurriedly carrying fans made of cardboard to resemble palms.*)

First Servant: Good morning, Pharaoh, did you sleep well?

Pharaoh: No, I did not. I had a terrible dream.

First Servant: I am sorry, your Majesty, could you tell it to me?.

Pharaoh: What good would that do? Can't you think of something else?

Second Servant: We could call the court magicians. Perhaps they could help you. Should I call them?

Pharaoh: Call them at once! (*Servants leave and enter with magicians.*)

First Magician: Let us hear this dream, your Majesty.

Second Magician: I will get the magic crystal. (*Goes offstage and returns with a glass bowl turned upside down.*)

Pharaoh: I dreamed that I saw seven fat cows come out of a river followed by seven lean cows. The seven lean cows ate the seven fat ones.

First Magician: Is that all you dreamed?

Pharaoh: No, I had still another dream of a similar nature.

Second Magician: Nothing appears in the magic crystal. Let us hear this dream, too.

Pharaoh: I saw seven well-formed ears of corn growing in the field. These were on a stalk

	and seven small ears of corn swallowed up the seven large ones.
First Magician:	I am very sorry, your Majesty, but nothing appears in the magic crystal. We cannot decipher this dream for you. (*They leave.*)
Pharaoh:	Oh, what shall I do? This is driving me mad! (*Rings for the butler. Butler enters and bows to the floor.*)
Butler:	What do you wish, your Majesty?
Pharaoh:	Go search for someone to interpret my dreams. I shall go mad until I know what they mean.
Butler:	When I was in prison there was a man named Joseph, who was there, too. Both the baker and I had dreams and he told us what they meant. It came to pass as he said.
Pharaoh:	Go at once and get this man. (*Butler bows and leaves, two servants enter and serve Pharaoh fruit and water.*) (*Butler enters with Joseph and they bow.*)
Butler:	This is Joseph whom you wish to see.
Pharaoh:	I had a dream. Can you tell me what it means? The magicians could not help me.
Joseph:	Tell me your dreams. God will give Pharaoh an answer to ease his mind.
Pharaoh:	I dreamed that I saw seven fat cows come up out of a river, followed by seven lean cows. The seven lean ones ate the seven fat ones. Then I dreamed that seven well-formed ears of corn were growing on a stalk and seven small ears also. The seven small ears ate the seven large ears.
Joseph:	Both of your dreams mean the same. God has told you what is going to happen. The seven good cattle are seven good years and the seven good ears of corn are seven good years. It means seven years of famine and they will follow seven years of plenty.
Pharaoh:	What shall we do?
Joseph:	Appoint a wise man to oversee the lands of Egypt for the seven years of plenty. Save all the grain and store it in large bins. Then your land shall not perish because of famine. Your people will not starve.
Butler:	That sounds like a good idea to me.
Servants:	To us, too. Find a good man, Pharaoh.
Pharaoh:	Where shall we find a good, wise man?
Servants:	Choose Joseph. He is wise. (*Joseph kneels.*) (*Humility.*)
Pharaoh:	(*Standing.*) Since God has chosen you to show this dream to me, there is none greater or wiser. I am still King but you are next in greatness. (*Places a ring on Joseph's finger that he takes from his own hand, and a chain from his own neck and places it around Joseph's neck.*) So shall it be! Go, servants, and bring Joseph fine clothes!
Narrator:	So Joseph was clothed in fine clothes and was made ruler over Egypt at the age of thirty. For seven years all the grain was put into huge bins. Through his wisdom the people were saved from starvation. Many people from other lands came to Egypt to buy grain. Among them were the very brothers that had sold Joseph into the hands of the merchants. They had to bow down to Joseph as he told them they would someday. Joseph made himself known to his brothers. They brought their wives and families into Egypt. Jacob was a happy man to know that his son still lived.

JOSEPH AND HIS BROTHERS

Words and Music by Helen Friesen

JESUS IS MY BEST FRIEND

by Margaret McKinney Baker

Cast: Mary—Kind, gentle girl who loves Jesus.
Martha—Mary's sister. She loves Jesus, too, but she is obsessed with housecleaning.
Jesus—God's Son, our Savior.
Narrator—May be male or female student or puppet.

Costumes: Mary, Martha and Jesus are dressed in biblical costumes. Narrator is dressed in modern clothing.

Stage Setting: Both scenes take place in the home of Mary and Martha.

Props: Bible for narrator. Small kitchen towels, pot holders, washcloths, pots and pans for sound effects.

Narrator: (*At stage left, reading from Bible: Luke 10:38-42.*)
"Now it came to pass, as they went, that he entered into a certain village: and a certain woman named Martha received him into her house. And she had a sister called Mary, which also sat at Jesus' feet, and heard his word.
But Martha was cumbered about much serving, and came to him, and said, Lord, dost thou not care that my sister hath left me to serve alone? bid her therefore that she help me.
And Jesus answered and said unto her, Martha, Martha, thou art careful and troubled about many things:
But one thing is needful: and Mary hath chosen that good part, which shall not be taken away from her."
The story takes place in the home of Mary and Martha, friends of Jesus, who live in Bethany. Mary is eagerly awaiting the arrival of Jesus, while Martha is inside frantically trying to clean house and prepare a meal for Jesus.
(*As Mary enters, sounds of pots and pans can be heard in the background. Towels, washcloths, etc., are being tossed lightly above the puppet stage to indicate frantic housecleaning. Mary calmly sings the beginning of "Jesus Is My Best Friend" as these actions are taking place.*)

Martha: (*Offstage, interrupting song in a loud, frantic voice.*) Mary, get in here and help me finish this cleaning. Jesus will be here soon.

Mary: (*Looking behind puppet stage, speaks calmly.*) In a minute, Martha. Right now I'm looking to see if Jesus is coming.
(*Mary continues with song.*)

Martha: (*Offstage, continuing to speak loudly and frantically to Mary.*) Jesus is my friend, too, but we've got to get this house ready for Him and I've not even started dinner. (*Pots and pans can be heard as she speaks of dinner.*)

Mary: Don't get so upset, Martha. We can clean house tomorrow, but today Jesus is coming and I don't want to miss one single minute of His visit. I'm going to wait right here until I see Him coming down the road.

Song: "Down the Road" (*Mary sings.*)

Mary:	(*In a very excited voice.*) Martha, come quickly! I see Jesus! He's coming. Hurry! (*Mary exits.*)
Martha:	(*Entering with a big sigh.*) Umph! She's a lot of help! Here Jesus is arriving and the house is a mess. The food is not cooked . . . What are we to do?
Song:	"What Are We To Do?" (Martha sings frantically.) (*After song, Martha exits. Mary and Jesus enter.*)
Mary:	(*Excitedly.*) Oh, Jesus, I'm so glad You're here! We've waited so long for You to come.
Jesus:	Thank you, Mary. It is good to see you again, but tell me, what is . . . .
Martha:	(*Enters and interrupts Jesus.*) Mary! I need your help in the kitchen. (*Turns to Jesus.*) Lord, don't you care that Mary has left all of the work for me to do?
Jesus:	(*Gently.*) Martha, Martha. You are troubled about so many things; only one thing is needful. Come, sit with me as Mary has done. Spend the day visiting with a friend who cares for you. (*All exit.*)
Narrator:	Scene II is the same setting; the home of Mary and Martha. It is the day after Jesus' visit. (*Mary and Martha enter.*)
Mary:	Oh, Martha, I enjoyed Jesus' visit so much yesterday. Didn't you, too?
Martha:	(*Hesitantly.*) Well . . . yes, but I certainly was upset with you for not helping me.
Mary:	Yes, I'm sorry you got upset, but I did not want to waste one minute during the Master's visit. We can clean house any time, but yesterday Jesus was here, and He is our best friend.
Song:	"Jesus Is My Best Friend" (*Both girls sing.*)

JESUS IS MY BEST FRIEND

Words and Music by Margaret McKinney Baker

WHAT ARE WE TO DO?

Words and Music by Margaret McKinney Baker

DOWN THE ROAD

Words and Music by Margaret McKinney Baker

FIVE LOAVES, TWO FISHES

by Margaret McKinney Baker

Scripture: John 6:5-14
Spiritual Concept: God can make the insignificant great for His glory.
Cast: James, Andrew, Rebecca, Naomi (four young teens)

James: Say, Andrew, whatcha got there?

Andrew: It's what's left of a barley loaf I brought from home.

James: It sure does look tasty. Could I have a bite?

Andrew: Well, maybe just a small . . . . (*Rebecca and Naomi enter at right stage, speaking loudly.*)

Rebecca: (*Interrupting.*) Say, Andrew, is that some of your mother's delicious barley bread?

Andrew: Yeah, Rebecca, it sure is. I was just getting ready to share with . . . .

Naomi: (*Interrupting.*) Oh, Andrew, could Rebecca and I have some? Your mom makes the best barley bread in the village.

Andrew: Well, there really isn't enough to share with all three of you.

James: Too bad we're not with that new rabbi again. He'd see to it that it would be enough.

Andrew: What new rabbi, James?

James: The one who . . . .

Rebecca: (*Interrupting.*) I've been hearing about him. Have you seen him, Naomi?

Naomi: No, but I've heard lots of kids talk about him. He sure does do a lot of miracles.

Andrew: What new rabbi, James?

James: The one who . . . .

Rebecca: (*Interrupting.*) The one who turned the water into wine at the wedding in Cana.

Naomi: Yeah, I heard the wine was even better than what the bridegroom had served first.

Andrew: What new rabbi, James?

James: The one who . . . .

Naomi: (*Interrupting.*) The one who made the blind man see. Did you see that, Rebecca?

Rebecca: No, Naomi, I didn't. As a matter of fact, I've not seen this rabbi; I've just heard about him.

Andrew: (*A little louder.*) What new rabbi, James?

James: (*Matching Andrew's volume.*) The one who . . . .

Naomi: (*Interrupting.*) I even heard that he fed over five thousand people the other day.

Rebecca: Five thousand! He must be rich to feed that many people.

James: That's what I've . . . .

Naomi: (*Interrupting.*) No, he's not rich. They say there was a little boy there who had brought his lunch and . . . .

James: (*Interrupting a little louder.*)That's what I've . . . .

Rebecca: (*Interrupting.*) Oh, I heard something about that. When it came time to eat, this little boy brought this rabbi his lunch and . . . .

Andrew: (*Interrupting with a very loud voice.*) What rabbi, James?

James: (*Replying in same volume.*) The one who . . . .

Naomi: (*Interrupting.*) Go on, Rebecca, what did the rabbi do with the little boy's lunch?

James: (*Shouting.*) He took my lunch, prayed and fed over five thousand men and their families!

Rebecca: My goodness, James, you don't have to yell. But did you say . . . .

Naomi: (*Interrupting.*) Did you say he took your lunch and . . .

James: (*Still shouting.*) Yes, I was the boy with the five loaves and two fishes!

Rebecca: Well forevermore, James, why didn't you say so? We've all been asking and you stood there and said nothing!

Naomi: Yeah, James, you said nothing at all.

Andrew: Girls, James and I have been . . . .

Rebecca: (*Interrupting.*) You'd think with something that big happening to you, that you'd want the whole world to know.

Naomi: Obviously James doesn't. We've been here for some time now and he still hasn't told us the whole story.

Andrew: (*With stern voice.*) Girls, James and I have been trying for some time now to discuss this rabbi, and every time we open our mouths, the two of you interrupt. Do you suppose you could be quiet long enough for James to tell us his story?

Girls: (*Subdued.*) We'll try.

James: Well, as I was saying . . . . (*He hesitates, looks at Naomi and continues.*) You're not going to interrupt me, are you?

Naomi: No, James, I won't interrupt.

James: Well, as I was saying . . . . . (*He hesitates, looks at Rebecca and continues.*) Are you sure you're ready to listen?

Rebecca: Yes, James, I'm ready to listen.

James: Well, as I was saying . . . . (*Hesitates, looks at both girls, then continues.*) I had packed a small lunch and was going out on the mountainside to hear the new rabbi. He preached so long that everyone became hungry. It was obvious that he had not brought along enough food for that many people.

Andrew: In the first place, how could he have fed that many people?

James: There are several men who travel with him, and they help. But when they began to talk about food, the helpers look my lunch and gave it to the rabbi. But a funny thing happened. He took my lunch, prayed, and then told his helpers to pass the food to the people. He just keep breaking off pieces, and kept breaking off pieces.

Rebecca: James, are you sure you're telling the truth? This sure sounds "fishy" to me.

James: Honest! He kept sending his helpers out with food until all the people had been fed. (*A long pause.*)

Naomi: Well . . . is that the end of the story?

James: No, but what happened next was just as strange as when he was breaking up the bread and fish.

Andrew: What happened?

James: Well, he told his helpers to pick up the leftovers so nothing would be lost, and when the man returned, they had twelve baskets full of leftovers.

Rebecca: That is strange. They started with only five loaves and two small fishes, and they finished with twelve baskets of leftovers! Wow!

Andrew: That is some kind of rabbi! I see what you mean now about my snack. He could make it enough for all four of us and even more.

Song: "Five Loaves, Two Fishes" (*After song, all exit.*)

FIVE LOAVES, TWO FISHES

Based on John 6:5-14

Words and Music by Margaret McKinney Baker

MOSES AND HIS PEOPLE

by Edith E. Cutting

Cast: Jochebed, Pharaoh's daughter, Moses, Narrator, Miriam, Aaron, Voice of God

Narrator: A long, long time ago, in the country of Egypt, an Israelite or Hebrew woman, named Jochebed, was about to have a baby. She would have been happy, but the new Pharaoh, the Egyptian king, had ordered that all Israelite boys were to be killed when they were born. What was Jochebed to do if her baby was a boy? (Exodus 1:8-17)

Scene I

(*Jochebed and her daughter are working in their kitchen.*).

Jochebed: Oh, Miriam, my daughter, how I wish we were in Canaan instead of this terrible land.

Miriam: But all our people are here in Egypt.

Jochebed: I know, but I wish we were all back home. If my baby were born a boy in Canaan, I could rejoice. Here, I can only hope the baby will be a girl.

Miriam: Thank God, Aaron was born before the dreadful decree.

Jochebed: I do thank God for that, but I can't help worrying about him. Suppose the Pharaoh orders all our children killed? And I worry about your father. At night, he is so tired he can scarely eat.

Miriam: Besides, last night Father had been beaten because he did not work fast enough.

Jochebed: Don't speak of that. I grieve, but can do nothing except bathe the wounds and try to ease the hurt.

Miriam: Do you think we will ever go back to Canaan?

Jochebed: God alone knows. He led Joseph here to help our people in time of famine. Maybe someday He will send a leader to take us back.

Miriam: Just think, Mother, perhaps the new baby will be the one when he grows up!

Jochebed: Oh, Miriam, what a gift from God that would be! But we must first pray that he will be spared to grow up.

Narrator: The baby was a boy, but Jochebed had thought of a plan for keeping him safe. (Exodus 2:1-3)

Scene II

(*Miriam is weaving a basket of bulrushes while her mother holds the baby.*)

Jochebed: Hurry, Miriam. We must have the basket ready soon.

Miriam: Yes, I know we can't keep the baby hidden much longer. He's already three months old.

Jochebed: If he should creep out of the house, an Egyptian might see him and tell.

Miriam: But your plan is sure to work.

Jochebed: I hope so. Tomorrow morning we will put the baby's basket in the reeds at the edge of the river, and the current can't carry it away.

Miriam: And when the Pharaoh's daughter comes to the river to bathe, she will wonder what is in the basket.

Jochebed: Don't forget to weave a cover for it. That will keep the baby safe from tipping out but leave him air to breathe.

Miriam: I like to weave. These bulrushes are strong and beautiful.

Jochebed: When you have finished, I will daub the outside with pitch. That will keep the water out.

Miriam: Oh, it will be a little ark, like the big one that Noah built so long ago which saved his family and all the other living creatures.

Jochebed: Just so, this one will save my son.

Narrator: Jochebed's plan worked out well. That morning she put the little ark in the edge of the river, and Miriam hid nearby. (Exodus 2:4-10)

Scene III

(*Pharaoh's daughter appears at the river bank. She speaks to her servants offstage.*)

Pharaoh's daughter: My maidservants, you may go down along the bank of the river. But, stay where I can call you. (*She moves to the edge of the water.*) Now, what is this caught in the rushes? A beautiful little ark! I shall open it. What treasure will I find? (*She opens the basket. The baby starts to cry.*) Oh, a treasure indeed. What a beautiful baby! Maidservants, come quickly!

Miriam: (*She appears before any servants can get there.*) Your Royal Highness, did you call?

Pharaoh's daughter: Yes. See what I have found.

Miriam: A baby! Whose can it be?

Pharaoh's daughter: It must be one of the Hebrew babies cast into the river to die. But it was cast in so lovingly in this basket cradle!

Miriam: Would Your Highness like a Hebrew nurse? I can find one to take care of the baby for you.

Pharaoh's daughter: Oh, yes. Go quickly and bring me one.

(*Miriam hurries offstage and comes back with her mother.*)

Miriam: Here is a woman who can nurse the child for you.

Pharaoh's daughter: Care for him, and I will pay you. (*She hands the baby to Jochebed.*) I shall call him Moses because I drew him out of the water.

Jochebed: I will care for him gladly, Your Highness.

Pharaoh's daughter: When he no longer needs a nurse, bring him to me. He shall grow up in the palace and be taught as a prince, but he shall be a son to me.

Narrator: Years passed. Although Moses lived in the palace, he knew that he was really Hebrew. (Exodus 2:11-15)

Scene IV

(*Jochebed and Miriam are in their home.*)

Jochebed: Often I think how good God has been to me. He saved my son Moses, and made him a fine young man, a prince. Who would have thought it?

Miriam: Yes. I wish Moses could visit us more often, but at least he knows we are his people.

Jochebed: Indeed he does. And whenever he can, he helps any Hebrew who has trouble.

Miriam: Oh, look. Here comes Aaron, hurrying. How can he be away from his work in the daytime?

Aaron: (*Entering.*) Mother, Moses has had to leave the country. He just told me to bring word to you.

Jochebed: Leave the country! Where is he? What happened?

Aaron: Two days ago he saw an Egyptian beating one of our people. In his anger, he killed the Egyptian and buried the body.

Jochebed: Not Moses!

Aaron: Yes, Moses. He could not bear such injustice. But yesterday, when he tried to settle a dispute between two Hebrews, they accused him of killing the Egyptian.

Miriam: Then it is known?

Aaron: Yes, Pharaoh has sent men to seize Moses.

Jochebed: Oh, no! Oh, my son! I saved him as a baby, but how can I save him now?

Aaron: Take courage, Mother. He has fled to the land of Midian. The Pharaoh's men cannot follow him there. He keeps us in his heart, and he will come back when God wills.

Narrator: More years passed. In the land of Midian, Moses worked as a shepherd. One day he heard God calling him, but he feared he could not do as God commanded. (Exodus 3:1-18; 4:10-16)

Scene V

(*Moses walks in front of Mount Horeb.*)

Moses: How strange. Is that fire? The bush does not burn. I must see this thing more closely.

Voice of God: Moses. Moses.

Moses: (*Stands still.*) Here am I.

Voice: Draw not nigh. Put off your shoes, for the place whereon you stand is holy ground.

(*Moses takes off his sandals.*)

Voice: I am the God of thy fathers. I shall speak to you, but hereafter no one else shall hear.

Moses: (*Falls flat with his face to the ground.*) Yes, my Lord, I hear You speak, and I listen.

(*Silence.*)

Moses: But my Lord God, who am I, a shepherd, to go unto Pharaoh?

(*Silence.*)

Moses: My God, the children of Israel will not believe me. What shall I say to them?

(*Silence.*)

Moses: I will do as You command. But my Lord, I am slow of speech. How can I speak for my people before a king?

(*Silence.*)

Moses: Yes, my Lord. Into the mouth of Aaron I will put the words that You command. Thus we will do Thy will.

Narrator: Moses returned to Egypt as God had commanded him. Aaron helped by speaking for him as God had promised. After talking with the Israelite elders, Moses, and Aaron went to the Pharaoh's palace. (Exodus 5:1-9)

Scene VI

(*The Pharaoh is on his throne. Moses and Aaron enter.*)

Pharaoh: Why are you here? You take my time. What is your plea?

Aaron: Your Highness, great Pharaoh, we come to bring you a message from the Lord, God of Israel. "Let my people go," He says. We are to go into the wilderness to hold a feast to our God.

Pharaoh: Who is this god that I should obey his voice? I don't know him, and I will not let Israel go.

Aaron: The God of the Hebrews has met with us. Let us go, we beg of you. Let us go only a three-days journey into the desert. There we will make sacrifice to Him.

Pharaoh: Three days! Do not be so foolish! You are wasting time already, letting your people stand idle. They would not think of such a thing if they were busy.

Aaron: It is the Lord, not the people, who commands us. He is the great God, and if we do not obey, He will send terrible punishment.

Pharaoh: I will no longer listen. You make me laugh with your demands. Go, now. Set your people to finding straw for their brickmaking. My officers will no longer provide straw. Each man will make as many bricks as before, but will find for himself the stubble to make them. Be not so lazy as to think of a three-day sacrifice. Go, now! Go!

(*Moses and Aaron leave.*)

Narrator: To punish the Egyptians, the Lord sent ten terrible plagues. After each one, though, the Pharaoh's heart was again hardened, and he refused to let the Hebrews go.
The first plague was of water turned to blood. There were the plagues of frogs, and of lice, and of flies. Then the cattle died. After that came a plague of boils, terrible sores on man and beast. A dreadful storm of hail and fire raged through the land. Whatever was left was eaten by swarms of locusts. For three days there was thick darkness in the land.
Finally came the most awful punishment of all. Every firstborn animal and child of the Egyptians died! (Exodus 12:30-36)

Scene VII

(*Pharaoh stands by his throne. Moses and Aaron enter, bowing.*)

Pharaoh: Rise up and get you forth among my people, both you and the children of Israel!

Aaron: Have we truly your permission to go, great Pharaoh?

Pharoah: Go quickly and serve your Lord as you have said.

Aaron: And may we take our flocks and herds? We shall need them for food and for sacrifice.

Pharaoh: Yes, yes, take everything, but be gone! (*They turn to go.*) Wait! Bless me also, for your God is a mighty one. But go quickly, or we are all dead men.

(*Moses and Aaron leave, but stop outside the throne room.*)

Moses: The women must bring only unleavened bread and their kneading troughs.

Aaron: Yes, I will tell them to hurry.

Moses: But the Lord commanded that we borrow silver, gold and clothing from the Egyptians. We must not go before Him in such pitiful clothing.

Aaron: We will do all the Lord commands. But let us do all quickly before He again hardens the Pharaoh's heart.

Narrator: And so it was that Moses started to lead his people, the Israelites, on their long journey from Egypt to the Promised Land. (Exodus 12:37-41)

Scene VIII

(*Moses, Aaron, Miriam, Jochebed are walking together in the wilderness.*)

Moses: Was everyone ready? I hope no one was left behind. Though we started in the darkness, it is already late in this day. We must hurry on lest the Pharaoh's heart be hardened again. He might send soldiers to turn us back.

Aaron: I passed on all your words. The shepherds with their flocks and the herdsmen with their cattle are already far ahead.

LET MY PEOPLE GO

Words by Helen Kitchell Evans
Music by Frances Mann Benson

QUEEN ESTHER

by Edith E. Cutting

Cast: Mordecai, Esther, King, Haman, Narrator

Narrator: The story of Queen Esther is a biblical Cinderella story with a difference. The first important difference is that Esther was a real person, but Cinderella was only make-believe. We know that the story of Esther is true because there is a whole book in the Old Testament about her. The book is called Esther.
Her story happened a long time ago, almost five hundred years before Jesus was born, but the people were all real. Esther was a Jewish girl who lived in Persia with her friends and relatives who had been exiled from Palestine. Her cousin Mordecai had brought her up after her mother and father had died. King Xerxes was a real king (called in this book, Ahasuerus), who lived in a real palace at Shushan and ruled all of the country of Persia. Haman was one of his chief officers. Now the story begins.

Scene I

(*Outside the palace. Esther enters from one side and Mordecai from the other.*)

Mordecai: Greetings, dear Esther. You have come early, as I asked.

Esther: Indeed yes, Cousin Mordecai. How could I not do as you asked? You have been like a father to me.

Mordecai: And you have been a daughter to me.

Esther: I am grateful, Cousin Mordecai, for your care all these years. Is there some trouble now? Is there some way I can serve you?

Mordecai: No trouble, at least not yet, but perhaps you can serve in days to come. Hear now this news. The great King Xerxes is planning to choose the most beautiful maiden in Persia and marry her. She will be his queen. All the fair young women are to be brought to the palace for him to see, and I want you to come with the others.

Esther: I, Cousin Mordecai? There are many others more beautiful than I. Besides, I am Jewish. Would a Persian king marry a humble Jewish girl?

Mordecai: You are not to say anything about being Jewish. Our God made you beautiful as you are. If you are chosen to be queen, the time may come when you can help your people. Who knows what trouble they may have? But for now, say nothing.

Esther: (*Bowing.*) Cousin Mordecai, I will do as you wish.

Mordecai: My blessings on you! Farewell for now.

(*He turns and goes out leaving Esther alone, thinking. Slowly she too turns and leaves.*)

Narrator: Over a year has passed since King Xerxes' decision to choose a new queen. Many beautiful girls from all parts of Persia have come before him and been sent away. The story continues.

Scene II

(*Inside the palace. The king is standing by his throne, with Haman a little behind him. Esther enters but stops, bowing, just inside the door*).

King: Come forward, fair maiden. What name shall I call you?

Esther: (*Walking a few steps toward him.*) My name is Esther, great king.

King: Esther! That name means star. You are indeed as beautiful as the evening star, with your dark hair and shining eyes.

Esther: (*Bowing again.*) You are most kind to say so, Your Highness.

King: (*Turning to Haman.*) Is she as good as she is beautiful, Haman? What do you know of her?

Haman: (*Steps forward.*) The king's chamberlain tells me this young maiden is the kindest of all maidens to her attendants, my lord.

King: And is she obedient and humble?

Haman: She has found favor in the sight of all. Your Highness will notice that she is dressed simply, as the chamberlain ordered, without extra gold or jewels.

King: (*Turning back to Esther.*) Then you shall have gold and jewels at my command. Come nearer, my star.

Esther: (*Comes forward.*) Your happiness is all the gold and jewels that I desire, Your Highness.

King: (*Lifting the crown and setting it on her head.*) It shall be my happiness to make you my queen. (*He turns to Haman.*) Haman, provide for a great feast seven days from today. Send messages and gifts to all the provinces of Persia. Let all my princes and my servants attend Queen Esther's feast!

Haman: It shall be as you wish, my lord. (*He hurries from the room.*) (*King Xerxes takes Esther's hand and leads her out the other way.*).

Narrator: If this had been a Cinderella story, it would have ended after the last scene, with the words, "and they lived happily ever after." But this is not the end of Queen Esther's story. It is only the beginning. Real danger and real happiness are to come to her. Now the time is many days after her marriage, and her Cousin Mordecai is waiting to see her.

Scene III

(*Outside the palace walls. Mordecai walks back and forth until Esther comes out.*)

Esther: Cousin Mordecai, you are so good to me. You come every day to see that all is well. But today you are early.

Mordecai: Yes, yes. I am very worried. You must sent word to the king at once. (*He walks closer and lowers his voice.*) His life is in danger!

Esther: (*Starts back.*) Our king's life?

Mordecai: Hush. Let me tell you. (*He comes closer yet.*) I have heard two of the great king's doorkeepers plotting against him. I will only whisper their names. (*He leans forward and whispers in her ear.*).

Esther: Oh, how terrible! I will send a message to King Xerxes at once. Wait for me here. (*She hurries away. Mordecai walks back and forth anxiously.*)

Haman: (*Enters and pauses before Mordecai.*) Are you forgetting to bow before me, Mordecai?

Mordecai: No, I do not forget. I just do not bow before you.

Haman: You must bow to me, I am King Xerxes' chosen officer.

Mordecai: I bow only to the king and to God.

Haman: You will be sorry you did not honor me! (*He leaves.*)

Esther: (*Comes back.*) The king has been told the names you whispered to me, and the men have been found.

Mordecai: Is our king safe?

Esther: Yes, and he will have your name recorded in his books. You have done him a great service. Go in peace, Cousin Mordecai. The wicked men will be punished, and King Xerxes will be safe, thanks to you.

Mordecai: And to you, my daughter.

(*Esther watches him leave, then she goes back inside the palace.*).

Narrator: Several days have passed, and Haman has decided how he is going to get a terrible revenge on Mordecai for not bowing to him. He will do it in such a way that even the king will not know Haman is plotting Mordecai's death. The story continues.

Scene IV

(*Inside the palace. King Xerxes and Haman are walking and talking together.*)

Haman: I must tell Your Highness some bad news I have just discovered.

King: What is that?

Haman: I have learned there is a certain group of people in your kingdom who do not follow your laws.

King: Not follow my laws! Where are these people who do not obey my laws? Who are they?

Haman: They are scattered throughout the land, Your Highness. They are known as Jews, and their laws are different from yours.

King: My laws shall be obeyed through all of Persia!

Haman: Of course, Your Highness. That is why I mentioned them. Your laws must be obeyed!

King: But what is to be done? Why have I not been told before? These people must be punished!

Haman: If it please the king, they must be more than punished. They must be destroyed as a lesson to other peoples.

King: But if they are scattered throughout Persia, how can this be done?

Haman: I have thought of a way, O King. Let it be written to all of your officers that on a certain day, these people who disobey you are to be killed. I will see to it. I will pay ten thousand talents of silver to see that they are destroyed, I mean to see that your will is carried out.

King: You are most loyal to me, Haman. I will trust your judgment. Here, take my ring. (*He hands it to Haman.*) The royal seal gives you authority over the people and their property. I do not want you to sacrifice your money to me. Keep your talents, but do as you think best with those people. See that messages are sent to all parts of my kingdom. After the messages are signed with my seal, return the ring to me. Then all those Jews will be destroyed on whatever day you name.

Haman: I will cast lots to see what day is best. You need think no more about it. I will do all as you have commanded. Now let us sit in the garden and enjoy a cooling drink. (*They go out together.*)

Narrator: When the news of the king's command to destroy the Jewish people is known, there is grief throughout the land. Mordecai puts on sackcloth as a sign of mourning and stands outside the palace walls, wailing for his people. Esther sends him good clothes to replace the sackcloth, but he will not accept them. The Bible tells us that a servant carried Esther's messages to Mordecai and his messages back to her, but both are so upset that we can imagine Esther's coming right out to talk with him.

Scene V

(*Outside the palace walls.*)

Esther: Cousin Mordecai, tell me why you are grieving. What is your trouble?

Mordecai: It is not my trouble alone. Have you not heard? All our people are to be killed. All Jewish people, young and old, men and women and even little children are to be destroyed on one certain day!

Esther: How can that be, Cousin Mordecai? We have lived here in peace for years.

Mordecai: I know, but that evil Haman has influenced the king. See, here is a copy of the decree. It has gone out through all of Persia.

Esther: But Cousin Moredecai, what can we do? It is too late. The king's decree cannot be changed.

Mordecai: It must be! You must ask him to change it. Now is the time to tell him these are your people. You must go to King Xerxes and plead for your people's lives.

Esther: Oh, Cousin Mordecai, I cannot go to the king unless he calls for me.

Mordecai: And why not? You are his queen!

Esther: You know I cannot. It is the law. Anyone who goes into his presence without being called will be killed unless King Xerxes himself holds out his golden sceptre. What good will it do if I go to him and am killed?

Mordecai: If all Jews are to be killed, you will not escape just because you are in the king's palace. If you won't speak for your people now, God will save them some other way. But you and all your family will be destroyed. Who knows but what the Lord God sent you here for this very purpose.

Esther: (*Walks back and forth thinking, then speaks.*) You are right. I will do as you say, Cousin Mordecai, but you must help me.

Mordecai: You know I will do all that I can.

Esther: You must gather all the Jews in the city to fast and to pray for me, for three days. My maidens and I will do the same. Then I will go to the king. (*She hesitates, then speaks firmly.*) I promise I will do as I have said. If I perish, I perish!

Mordecai: God be with you. We shall do as you say. (*He leaves and Esther goes back inside.*)

Narrator: Mordecai sends word to Jewish people all over the city of Shushan to fast and pray for Esther's safety and the success of her plea. Esther and her maidens also fast and pray. At last the three days come to a close, and Esther bravely enters the king's throne room without having been invited.

Scene VI

(*Inside the palace. King Xerxes stands alone by his throne. Esther enters but stands fearfully just inside the door. The king stares at her, but finally lowers his sceptre and holds it out toward her.*)

King: What brings my queen to me this day?

Esther: (*Walks forward, bows, and touches the tip of the sceptre.*) I hope you are not angry that I have intruded on your peace.

King: No, indeed. I am happy to see my beautiful Esther. What can I do to make you happy?

Esther: If it please Your Highness, I have come to ask a favor of my king.

King: Speak then, and say what it may be.

Esther: I would that my king and his chief officer, Haman, would come this day to a banquet that I have prepared for them.

King: That is a happy favor indeed.

Esther: Then you will come?

King: I shall come with delight. Let us now call Haman and tell him of your invitation. (*He claps his hands.*) Haman!

Haman: (*Enters and bows.*) My lord, what is it that I can do for you?

King: You will be pleased to know that my queen, the beautiful Esther, has invited you with me to her apartments for a feast she has prepared. See that no other plans interfere.

Haman: I am honored indeed. I look forward to this pleasure. Shall I now have Queen Esther escorted back to her apartments?

Esther: That is not necessary. My maidens wait outside for me. I shall be honored by your presence. (*She leaves. Then Haman and the king also leave.*)

Narrator: That evening the king cannot sleep. He has a servant read to him from the book of records. When the servant reads Mordecai's warning about the gatekeepers who plotted against the king, Xerxes is disturbed and sends the servant away to call Haman. Then the king walks about his room, thinking and talking to himself.

Scene VII

King: How could I have been so ungrateful as not to reward Mordecai? His telling me about those traitors saved my life. How can I make that up to him?

Haman: (*Enters.*) Your Highness sent for me?

King: Greetings to you, Haman. I have a question to ask. How can I best honor a man with whom I am pleased?

Haman: (*He hesitates.*) You might let him seem like a king for a day. Let him be dressed in one of your robes, and let the royal crown be placed on my head—I mean, his head. (*He struts back and forth.*)

King: Yes, I could do that.

Haman: And let him be mounted on one of your favorite horses, with a royal prince like a servant to lead the horses through the street. You could even have an announcer proclaim the honor before me—I mean, before him!

King: That is good. That lets everyone know why I honor him.

Haman: Your Highness is most generous to his friends.

King: Make haste, then. Take that robe I wore yesterday, and the crown, and a horse from the royal stables. You shall lead the horse to honor Mordecai, the Jew who saved my life.

Haman: Mordecai?

King: Yes, you remember Mordecai, the man who warned me of the traitors. Do all you have said and fail not.

Haman: (*Bows deeply to hide his angry face.*) It shall be as you say, my lord. (*He backs out of the room.*)

Narrator: Later the next day after Mordecai is honored, the feast to which Queen Esther had invited King Xerxes and Haman continues. Queen Esther had provided rich foods as well as entertainment to make sure that the king was enjoying himself before she made her special plea. Now on the second day she greets the king and Haman as they enter the banquet room.

Scene VIII

Esther: Welcome to the banquet prepared in your honor, King Xerxes and mighty Haman. You do me great honor by attending.

King: Indeed, you honor us by this magnificent feast. Now what may I do in return? Whatever you ask shall be done, even to half of my kingdom.

Esther: (*Bowing deeply.*) If I have found favor in your sight, o merciful king, let my life be spared and the lives of my people also.

King: What do you mean? Who threatens the life of my queen? Who dares to do so?

Esther: (*Pointing to Haman.*) That man! The wicked Haman has asked that all Jews be put to death, and I am Jewish. All my people and I are to be destroyed.

King: My queen to be destroyed! That cannot be! And my trusted officer at fault! I am so angry I must walk in the garden to restore my thoughts. (*He goes out.*)

Haman: (*Falling flat before Queen Esther.*) Oh, please, good Queen Esther, save me. The king is angry indeed, but I did not know you were Jewish. I will do anything.

King: (*Coming back in.*) Not my queen, but Haman, who planned this evil deed, shall die. He shall be hanged high on the gallows. Go from my sight! (*Haman crawls out.*)

Esther: Your Highness, I beg that you cancel the order to kill all Jews.

King: That cannot be. The king's order cannot be reversed!

Esther: (*Bowing deeply.*) Oh, great King Xerxes, if it seem good to you, let my Cousin Mordecai, whom you have honored, come before you. Grant that he too may plead for my people.

King: (*Walks back and forth thinking, then claps his hands and shouts for a servant.*) Bring Mordecai to me. (*The king and Esther stand silent while they wait. Then Mordecai enters.*)

King: I have a plan, Mordecai. Write to every province and seal the letter with this, my ring. (*Hands it to him.*) Say that all Jews may gather and defend themselves on the day they are attacked. If they are as brave as my queen, her people may save themselves.

Mordecai: I will do so gladly, my honored king. The day that was to have been a day of grief shall be a day of rejoicing for all generations.

King: So be it. Go now, and let all honor for this joy be given to my beautiful Queen Esther forevermore! (*Mordecai hurries out one way; Xerxes and Esther walk slowly out the other.*)

THE PRODIGAL SON

by Helen Kitchell Evans

A playlet based on Luke 15:11-32
Cast: Father, Two sons, Servants, Farmer

Scene I

(*This scene takes place in Father's house.*)

Youngest Son: Father, please give me the portion of goods that I would inherit. I want to take a journey into a far country. I am tired of staying here at home.

Father: I beg of you to stay.

Youngest Son: No, Father, I must seek my fortune in a far country.

Father: But where will you go?

Youngest Son: I do not know. I just need to leave home.

Scene II

(*This scene takes place in another country.*)

Farmer: What is it you want? You look like you have been traveling for a long time. What is your problem?

Prodigal Son: Oh, please help me. I am starving. I have spent all my money foolishly. I left my good home. My father does not know where I am. I am a no-good person!

Farmer: (*Hands bucket to him.*) You can feed the swine. (*He leaves.*)

Prodigal Son: No one in my father's house is hungry. The servants eat better than I do. I will return to my father. (*Sets bucket down and leaves stage.*)

Scene III

(*This scene takes place near his father's house.*)

Father:	I see someone coming down the road.
Servant:	It looks very much like your son that left home. (*Puts hands to eyes to look.*) Yes, yes, it is your son!
Father:	(*Runs to meet him, they embrace.*) My son! My son!
Prodigal Son:	My father, my good father. I am not worthy to be called your son. I will be your hired servant. I have spent all my money foolishly. I have sinned. (*Hangs head.*)
Father:	My son is home! (*To servants.*) Bring the food! Bring him the finest robe you can find. Bring him shoes and rings of gold. (*Servants leave and return with items mentioned. They place clothes on the son.*)
Prodigal Son:	My father! My wonderful father! It is so nice to be home again. There is no place in the world like home.
Father:	(*To servants.*) Go bring the fatted calf! Let us all be happy!
Elder Son:	(*Enters.*) What is the noise all about?
Servant:	Your brother has returned.
Elder Son:	Father, I have served you all these years. You have never held a feast for me.
Father:	Son, you have been very good. You have stayed with your old father. I love you very much. All that is mine is yours, but let us not hate. This is your brother who was lost and is now found. Come. (*Elder brother moves toward younger brother. They embrace. They leave stage together. Others follow.*) (*This last part of the scene should take place slowly, giving it the dramatic expression needed for this scene.*)

THE THINGS JESUS TAUGHT US

Words and Music by Kathy Jones

CREATIVE COSTUMES

by Marilyn Senterfitt

The play is selected, the cast is chosen, the lines are being memorized, the music is being practiced. There remains only one last obstacle, the costumes. Many play organizers find costumes the hardest task of all in bringing a play together. To ease that burden, here are some suggestions for a variety of biblical costumes.

A BASIC PATTERN

To begin with, ask for donations of twin-sized sheets in solid colors or in stripes. You may also use 6 yards of 36-inch fabric that has been cut into two 3-yard lengths and sewn together. Fold sheet or fabric in half lengthwise. Fold again from top to bottom. Cut a pattern like the one shown. Adjustments can be made for hem and arm length for each child. Stitch the side seams and underarm seams. Hem all raw edges by turning up once. This simple pattern makes a loose fitting robe.

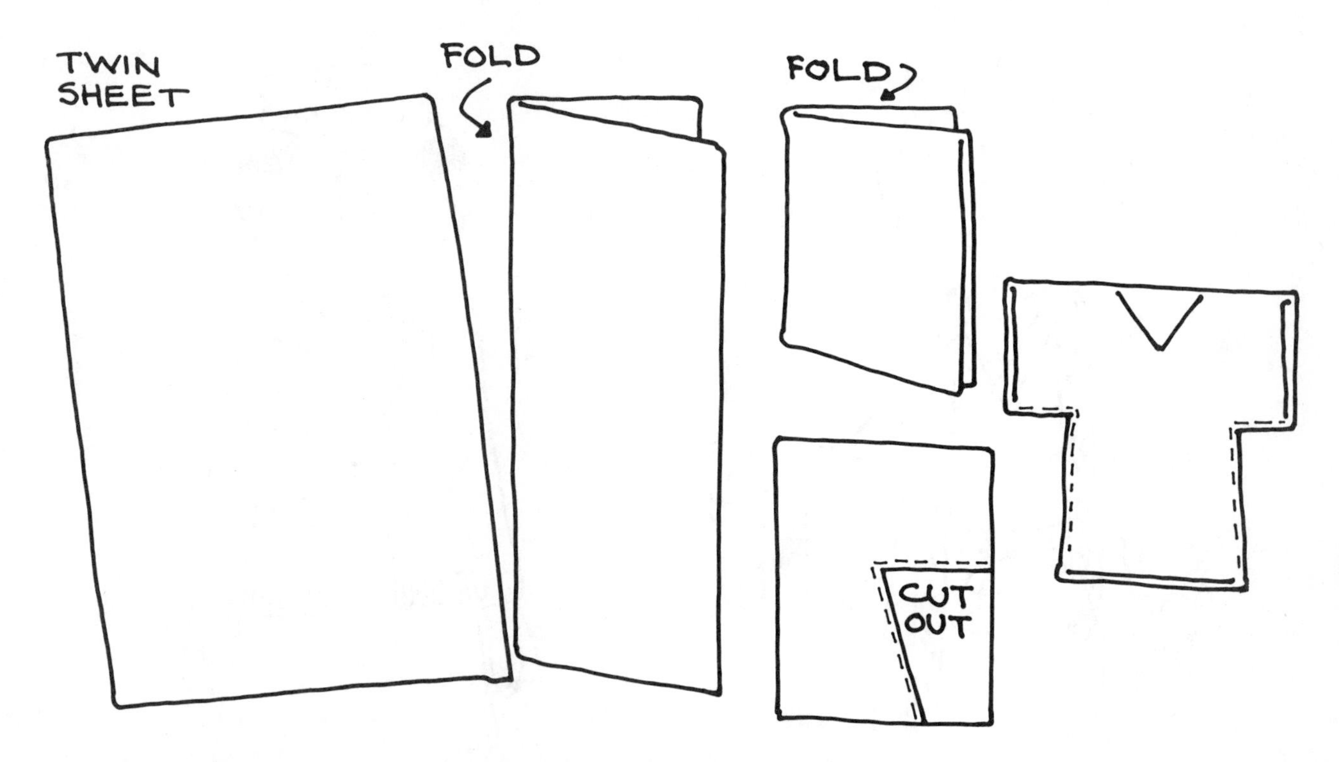

PATTERN VARIATIONS

Sleeveless Vest: Follow the instructions, but cut pattern, omitting the long sleeve. Then cut from neck to hem in front and turn back raw edges. Vest may be worn over a long robe.

Tunic: Follow instructions but cut sleeves shorter and cut length of robe shorter. This may be worn over a long robe. Other suggested uses follow.

COSTUMES FOR ROYALTY AND PRIESTS

Royalty: All kings, queens, etc. can wear bright colors with several pieces of jewelry. The addition of gold or silver braid to the hem and sleeves will add more color. Crowns can be constructed from gold poster board and adorned with braid, sequins, or fake gem stones. Cut strips of poster board and staple ends to form a circle. Cover with foil or gold paper and use as headbands, armbands, or bracelets.

High Priest: An accurate costume needs a long robe, a shorter tunic and a sleeveless tunic worn over both. The latter should be made of a brocade-like material. Attach a row of small bells to the longer tunic. A breastplate can be made from an 8-inch square of gold poster board. Attach a cord to slip over head and glue 12 gem stones in four rows on the square. These represent the twelve tribes of Israel. Other priests should be dressed in white. Check a Bible dictionary for details on this or any other costume you may need.

KING OR QUEEN

HIGH PRIEST

SHEPHERDS AND ANGELS

Shepherds: Robes can be made from a striped sheet or burlap-like material. Drapery fabric would be fine. Make headcoverings with a 36″ x 36″ piece. Center on head and secure with a stretchy headband, cord or strip of fabric. Shepherds will enjoy finding their own tree limb or other wood to use as a crook.

Angels: Use a white twin-sized sheet for the robe. You can omit wings and add gold braid or rickrack around neck and hem. Belt should have same gold trim. A headband as described earlier can also be added.

COSTUMES FOR WOMEN AND CHILDREN

Women: A headcovering made in the same way as those for the shepherds can be used. It can be held in place with a band or bobby pins. A tunic worn over the long robe of a contrasting color will make a more elaborate costume. As with any costume, the addition of braid or rickrack will bring the costume to life.

Children: Use a shorter version of the robe or tunic and hem at the knee. Belt with cord or a strip of fabric. Children may be shoeless or wear thongs.

SOLDIERS

Use the tunic pattern. Make a breastplate from two 12-inch squares of poster board. Punch holes in corners. Secure over shoulders with two lengths of yarn. Attach at lower sides with two lengths of yarn. The breastplate will cover the top front and back of the tunic. Cut out several 12 to 14-inch pointed strips from poster board. Punch holes in unpointed ends. String strips of yarn or cord and tie around waist under the breastplate. Make a sword and shield with a handle from poster board.

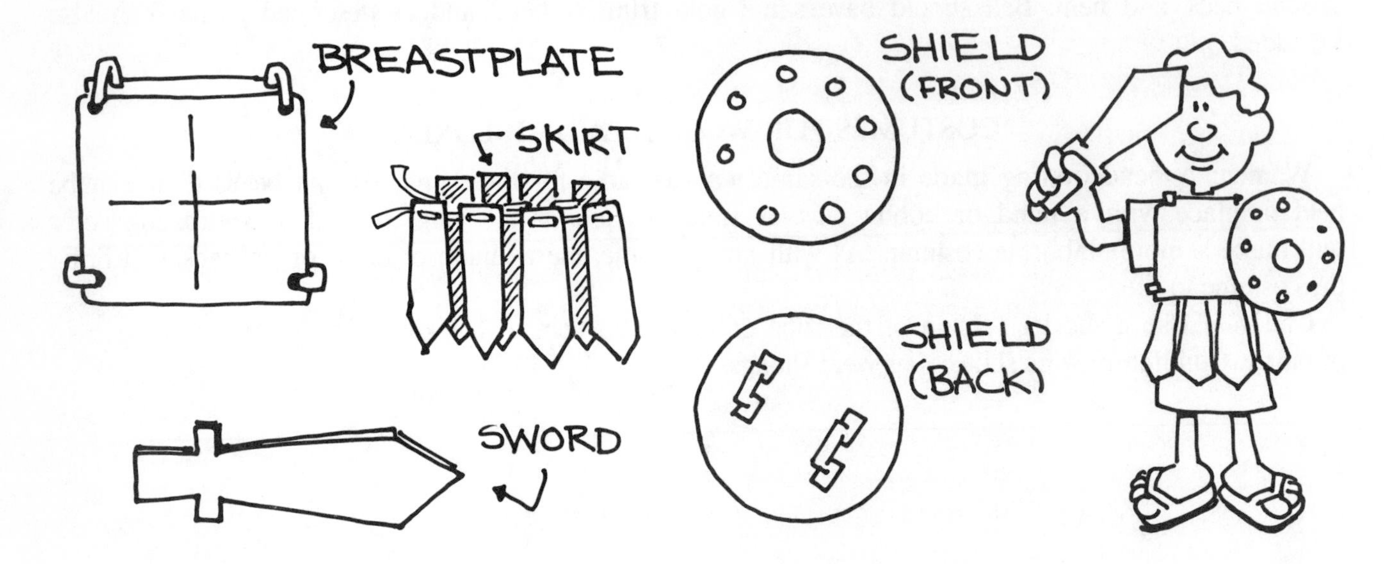

A COSTUME CHECK-OUT

The play is over, the audience has departed and the children have left their costumes in a pile at your feet. What now?

Why not make these costumes available to all the organizations of the church. They may be stored on a clothes rack and labeled by character: shepherd, priest, angel, etc. All the accessories can be placed in marked boxes. Advertise the availability of the costumes. Bible lessons will come to life as children are encouraged to dress up and act out the story. Older children could write their own biblical stories and perform the skit or play for younger classes, nursing homes or shut-ins. A camera and roll of slide film would give children the opportunity to pose scenes from a Bible story, write their narration, and show the slide story to the church or other groups.

These costumes could be checked out in much the same way as a teacher checks out a reference book from the church library. A collection of creative costumes can prove to be an exciting new teaching tool.

SCENERY PATTERNS

Flannel Board Cutouts
Bulletin Board Patterns
Clip 'N' Copy Graphics

The reproducible biblical figures on this and the four pages that follow can be used in dozens of creative ways to make your biblical studies more joyful. Here are a few tips for using the biblical graphics:

1. Use an overhead projector to enlarge for play scenery.
2. Reproduce on light cardboard. Cut out and attach flannel strips to the back of each figure for telling Bible stories found on pages 6-34.
3. Use an overhead projector to enlarge figures for bulletin boards.
4. Use as graphics to be added to performance invitations or programs. Duplicate as needed and have children decorate each with markers, crayons, paint and glitter.
5. Reduce to make patterns for Bible stickers and awards. (Most print shops can reproduce copy to any size desired.)
6. Use an overhead projector to enlarge figures for a hall mural. Include Bible verses for each mural. Decorate with colored chalk to make soft, pastel murals.
7. Reproduce on light cardboard. Give each student an appropriate set of figures and yarn to create his/her own Bible story mobile. Punch holes in the top and bottom of figures and tie together in a balanced fashion.

Enlarge using overhead projector.

Use graphics for invitations or programs.

Create a hall mural.

Create a Bible mobile.

BIBLE STORY INDEX